Interactive SCIENCE

TEKS Preparation and Study Guide

grade 8

PEARSON

ISBN-13: 978-0-13-324441-0
ISBN-10: 0-13-324441-5
1 2 3 4 5 6 7 8 9 10 V016 17 16 15 14 13

Contents

★ Texas Standardized Test Prep

This TEKS Preparation and Study Guide focuses on the Grade 8 curriculum required by the *Texas Essential Knowledge and Skills* (TEKS).

The workbook follows the Table of Contents of Pearson's *Texas Interactive Science Student Edition*. It provides lesson summaries and comprehensive assessments for each lesson in the student edition.

Following the lessons is a cumulative review for each chapter. Also included at the back of the workbook is a collection of Test-Taking Strategies to help you prepare for end-of-the-year testing.

Review and Practice

Review the main ideas for each lesson and build knowledge of science vocabulary.

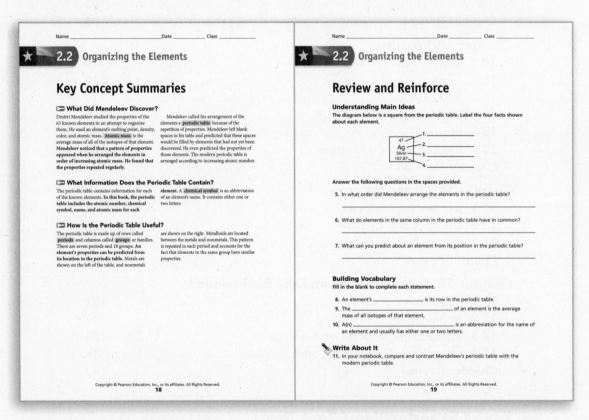

▲ The **Key Concept Summaries** review the main points of each lesson and include the lesson's vocabulary, highlighted and bold for quick access. The Key Concept Summaries can be used both as summation for a lesson or a review before assessment.

▲ The **Review and Reinforce** page gives you the opportunity to show what you have learned. The questions vary in format and difficulty level so you can practice comprehension in many different ways.

★Texas Standardized Test Prep

Chapter Reviews and Test-Taking Strategies give you the opportunity to practice test-taking skills. The Grade 6 and 7 Supporting TEKS Review provides you with an overview of TEKS from past grades.

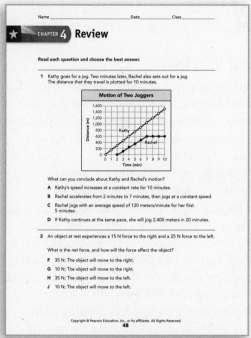

▲ The 2-page **Chapter Review** assesses the main points of the chapter.

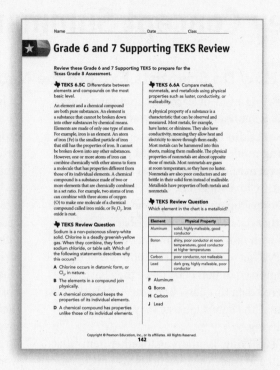

▲ The 12-page **Grade 6 and 7 Supporting TEKS Review** refreshes TEKS from earlier grades that you may be tested on in end-of-the-year tests.

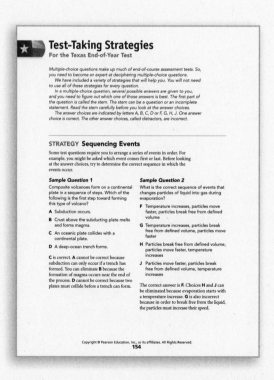

◄ Each **Test-Taking Strategy** includes helpful tips, along with two sample questions that show how the strategy can be applied.

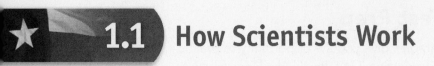

1.1 How Scientists Work

Key Concept Summary

🔑 How Do Scientists Explore the Natural World?

Science is a way of learning about the natural world. **Scientists explore the natural world by using skills such as observing, classifying, making models, inferring, and predicting. They form and test their ideas through scientific investigation.**

Observing means using one or more senses to gather data. A quantitative observation deals with numbers, or amounts. A qualitative observation deals with descriptions that cannot be expressed in numbers. Once they have gathered data through observing, scientists must organize the data. One way they do this is by classifying.

Classifying is grouping together items that are alike in some way. Scientists also make models to help them study things that cannot be observed directly. To explain or interpret things they have observed, scientists use inferring. Inferences are based on reasoning from prior knowledge and what was observed.

Predicting means making a statement or a claim about what will happen in the future based on past experience or evidence. While inferences are attempts to explain what has already happened, predictions are forecasts about what will happen. Analyzing involves evaluating observations and data to reach a conclusion about them. Scientists use all these skills in scientific investigations. A scientific investigation is the forming and testing of ideas about the natural world.

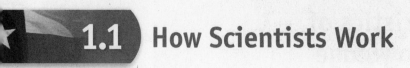

1.1 How Scientists Work

Review and Reinforce

Understanding Main Ideas
Answer the following questions in your notebook.

1. What skills do scientists use to help them form and answer questions about the natural world?

2. What is the difference between quantitative and qualitative observations?

3. How does making models help scientists observe?

4. What is the difference between inferring and predicting?

Building Vocabulary
Match each term with its definition by writing the letter of the correct definition in the right column on the line beside the term in the left column.

5. _____ predicting

a. an observation dealing with numbers or amounts

6. _____ observing

b. explaining or interpreting observations

7. _____ qualitative observation

c. grouping together items that are alike in some way

8. _____ inferring

d. evaluating observations and data to reach conclusions

9. _____ science

e. using one or more senses to gather information

10. _____ analyzing

f. an observation that deals with descriptions that cannot be expressed in numbers

11. _____ quantitative observation

g. making a statement or claim about what will happen in the future

12. _____ classifying

h. a way of learning about the natural world

Write About It

13. In your notebook, explain how the skills of science are part of a scientific investigation.

1.2 The Characteristics of Scientific Knowledge

Key Concept Summaries

🔑 What Do Scientific Investigations Involve?

Scientists use skills such as observing and inferring in scientific investigations. They also have certain attitudes, such as skepticism. Skepticism is an attitude of having doubt. **In addition to the skills and attitudes of scientists, scientific investigations involve collecting evidence in a scientific way and using that evidence to make inferences and to reach conclusions.**

Data are facts, figures, and other evidence collected during a scientific investigation. Empirical evidence is data that are collected using scientific processes and that describe particular observations.

Scientists use logical reasoning to examine their data and draw conclusions based on patterns in their data. All scientific investigations involve the collection of relevant empirical evidence.

🔑 What Are Scientific and Pseudoscientific Thinking?

There are two general types of reasoning: objective reasoning and subjective reasoning. Objective reasoning is based on evidence. Subjective reasoning is based on personal feelings or personal values. If you base your conclusion on your personal feelings, you could reach an incorrect conclusion.

A pseudoscience is a set of beliefs that may make use of science but that is not based on

observation, objective reasoning, or scientific evidence. **Science is based on empirical evidence and well-reasoned interpretation of data. Pseudoscience may make use of scientific data. But the conclusions of pseudoscience are based on subjective reasoning, faulty reasoning, or faulty beliefs, not on careful examination of evidence.**

🔑 What Characterizes Science and Its Methods?

Science is characterized by an ordered approach to learning about the world. This approach relies on using skills to collect empirical data, analyzing the data to find patterns that lead to inferences and trends, and using objective reasoning to reach conclusions.

Although science is based on empirical evidence and objective reasoning, its results are open to change. Sometimes new patterns contradict existing patterns. Scientists must then throw out their old conclusions.

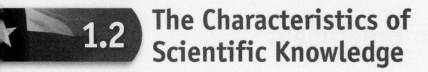

Review and Reinforce

Understanding Main Ideas

Answer the following questions in the spaces provided.

1. How do scientists analyze empirical evidence?

_____

_____

_____

2. Give one example of a pseudoscientific idea and one example of a scientific idea.

_____

_____

_____

3. How might the conclusions drawn from scientific investigations change?

_____

_____

_____

Building Vocabulary

Match each term with its definition by writing the letter of the correct definition in the right column on the line beside the term in the left column.

4. _____ empirical evidence

5. _____ objective reasoning

6. _____ skepticism

7. _____ pseudoscience

8. _____ subjective reasoning

9. _____ data

a. facts, figures, and other evidence

b. based on evidence

c. based on personal feelings or values

d. an attitude of doubt

e. data and observations collected through a scientific process

f. set of subjective beliefs

1.3 Designing an Experiment

Key Concept Summaries

What Is Scientific Inquiry?

Scientific inquiry is the process of gathering evidence about the natural world and proposing explanations based on this evidence. The first steps in the scientific inquiry process are posing questions and defining a problem. Next, you develop a hypothesis, which is a possible answer to a scientific question. In science, a hypothesis must be testable. Researchers perform investigations and collect data that either support or fail to support a hypothesis.

How Do You Design an Experimental Investigation?

You can design an investigation that follows reliable scientific principles to test a hypothesis. A large part of designing an experiment is controlling variables. The one factor that is purposely changed to test a hypothesis is the independent variable. The factor that may change in response to the independent variable is the dependent variable. A scientific experiment in which only one variable is changed at a time is called a controlled experiment. If the variables in an experiment are not controlled, it is impossible to tell which variable influenced the results. When designing experiments, scientists also have to be careful not to introduce experimental bias, or an error in the design of the experiment. Before starting an experiment, scientists determine what observations to make and what data to gather. Scientists use the International System of Units (SI), which is a system of units used to measure the properties of matter, to collect and record quantitative data. After data have been collected, they need to be interpreted. Then a conclusion is drawn. When drawing a conclusion, examine the data objectively to see if the results support or fail to support the hypothesis. Many trials are needed before a hypothesis can be accepted as true. A repeated trial is a repetition of an experiment. Scientists communicate their results with others. When scientists share their results, they describe their procedure and data so that others can repeat their experiments. A replication is an attempt by different scientists to conduct the same experiment.

What Is a Scientific Explanation?

In some branches of science it is difficult or impossible to perform experimental investigations. Scientists in these fields must develop a scientific explanation. A scientific explanation is a generalization that makes sense of observations by using logical reasoning. Things in the natural world that cannot be studied through a controlled experiment often rely on scientific explanation.

1.3 Designing an Experiment

Review and Reinforce

Understanding Main Ideas
Answer the following questions in your notebook.

1. What is the function of a hypothesis in the scientific inquiry process?

2. What role do independent and dependent variables play in an experimental investigation?

3. Why are repeated trials required before accepting a hypothesis as true?

4. How do scientists develop scientific explanations about subjects that are impossible to study through controlled experiments?

Building Vocabulary
Match each term with its definition by writing the letter of the correct definition in the right column on the line beside the term in the left column.

5. _____ controlled experiment

6. _____ hypothesis

7. _____ repeated trial

8. _____ dependent variable

9. _____ scientific explanation

10. _____ experimental bias

11. _____ scientific inquiry

12. _____ independent variable

13. _____ replication

a. a repetition of an experiment

b. a generalization that makes sense of observations by using logical reasoning

c. an error in the design of the experiment

d. the factor that is purposely changed to test a hypothesis

e. the process by which people gather evidence about the natural world and propose explanations based on this evidence

f. an attempt by a different group of scientists to conduct the same experiment

g. the factor that may change in response to the independent variable

h. a possible answer to a scientific question

i. a scientific experiment in which only one variable is changed at a time

Write About It
14. In your notebook, list the steps in the scientific inquiry process.

1.4 Models and Systems

Key Concept Summaries

How Do Scientists Use Models?

A model is any representation of an object or a process. **Scientists use models to test their ideas about things they cannot observe directly.** Physical models—drawings or three-dimensional objects—might be used to show things that are very small or very large. A computer program might be used to model a process, such as the movement of the stars as seen from Earth.

What Are the Characteristics of a System?

A system is a group of parts that work together to carry out a function. Examples include large systems such as Earth and small systems such as bicycle pumps.

All systems have at least one input, at least one process, and at least one output. An input is a material or the energy that goes into the system. A process is an action or series of actions that happen within the system. An output is the material or energy that comes out of a system. Feedback is output that changes a system in some way. When you exercise, your heart receives feedback that makes it pump faster.

How Do Models Help Scientists Understand Systems?

Scientists build models to represent a process. They test whether the input and output from the model match the input and output of the system in the natural world. Some systems that scientists study are simple. Such systems have only a few parts or only a few steps. Other systems are more complex. Many parts and variables can interact in complex systems. Often scientists use computers to keep track of the variables.

Because complex systems are difficult to model, scientists may model the specific part of the system that they wish to study. For example, to predict where a hurricane will make landfall, scientists might try to model winds that affect the hurricane's path.

When scientists construct a model of a system, they begin with certain assumptions. Scientists check their assumptions. They compare the input and output of the model to the input and output in the natural world. Sometimes scientists make assumptions to simplify the model.

1.4 Models and Systems

Review and Reinforce

Understanding Main Ideas

If the statement is true, write _true_. If the statement is false, change the underlined word or words to make the statement true.

1. _____ Scientists build <u>theories</u> to test their ideas about things that they cannot observe directly.

2. _____ Scientists test their <u>data</u> by comparing the input and output of their models to the input and output of the system in the natural world.

3. _____ Models allow scientists to predict <u>stability</u> in a system as a result of feedback or input changes.

Building Vocabulary

Match each term with its definition by writing the letter of the correct definition in the right column on the line beside the term in the left column.

4. _____ process

5. _____ output

6. _____ feedback

7. _____ model

8. _____ input

9. _____ system

a. action or series of actions that happen in a system

b. material or energy that goes into a system

c. representation of an object or process

d. changes a system in some way

e. material or energy that comes out of a system

f. group of parts that work together to carry out a function

 Write About It

10. In your notebook, identify the parts of a system. Then explain how scientists check to determine whether models they build are effective.

 **1.5** Safety in the Science Laboratory

Key Concept Summaries

Why Prepare for a Scientific Investigation?

Preparation helps to keep you safe when you perform a scientific investigation. It also keeps any living things you use safe. Science investigations can take place in the laboratory or in the field. The field is any area outside the science laboratory.

Whenever you perform a scientific investigation, your primary concern should be your safety and the safety of others. Always follow your teacher's instructions and the directions exactly.

Before an investigation, make sure you know its safety symbols. Safety symbols alert you to possible sources of accidents. Familiarize yourself with any equipment you will be using. Then, clean and organize your area. Label any containers you will be using.

You may work with plants and animals in the laboratory. Or you may encounter them in the field. Treat all living things with care and respect. Follow the animal care instructions provided.

What Should You Do If an Accident Occurs?

Sometimes accidents occur during an investigation. **Always alert your teacher first. Then follow your teacher's directions, and carry them out quickly.** Familiarize yourself with

the location and proper use of all the emergency equipment in the laboratory. Knowing safety and first-aid procedures beforehand will prepare you to handle accidents properly.

 **1.5** **Safety in the Science Laboratory**

Review and Reinforce

Understanding Main Ideas

Answer the following questions in the spaces provided.

1. List two reasons for good preparation before an investigation.

_____

_____

2. What two things should you follow during an investigation to maintain safety?

_____

_____

3. Describe how to properly care for animals during investigations.

_____

_____

Building Vocabulary

Fill in the blank to complete each statement.

4. The _____ is any area outside a science laboratory.

5. A(n) _____ symbol is used when you need to protect your clothes.

6. A(n) _____ symbol is used when you need to protect your hands from chemicals.

7. A(n) _____ symbol is used when you need to protect your eyes from chemical splashes, glass breakage, and sharp objects.

 Write About It

8. In your notebook, list three kinds of safety equipment that you wear and what they protect.

 **1.6** Science, Society, and You

Key Concept Summaries

🔑 Why Is Scientific Literacy Needed?

Because science is a big part of your world, you need scientific literacy. Scientific literacy means understanding scientific terms and principles well enough to ask questions, evaluate information, and make decisions. **By having scientific literacy, you will be able to identify good sources of scientific information, evaluate them for accuracy, and apply the knowledge to your life.**

To evaluate scientific information, you must first distinguish between evidence and opinion. In science, evidence includes observations and conclusions that have been repeated. It may or may not support a scientific claim. An opinion is an idea that may be formed from evidence but has not been confirmed by evidence.

🔑 How Do You Analyze Scientific Claims?

Scientific literacy helps you analyze scientific claims. **You can use scientific reasoning to analyze scientific claims and scientific** **explanations by looking for bias and errors in the research, evaluating data, and identifying faulty reasoning.**

🔑 How Do You Research Scientific Questions?

Chances are you will need to answer scientific questions to make decisions in your life. In science, you also need to do research to design an experiment.

To make decisions and design experiments, you need relevant and reliable background information. Relevant information is knowledge

that relates to the question. Reliable information comes from a person or organization that is accurate and not biased. Generally, universities, museums, and government agencies are sources of reliable information. So are many nonfiction books, magazines, and educational Web sites.

1.6 Science, Society, and You

Review and Reinforce

Understanding Main Ideas
Answer the following questions in the spaces provided.

1. What is the benefit of having scientific literacy?

   _____

   _____

   _____

2. How might you go about analyzing a scientific claim?

   _____

   _____

3. What would you need to make a decision or design an experiment about a certain scientific topic?

   _____

Building Vocabulary
Match each term with its definition by writing the letter of the correct definition in the right column on the line beside the term in the left column.

4. _____ evidence

    a. includes observations and conclusions that have been repeated

5. _____ scientific literacy

    b. understanding scientific terms and principles well enough to ask questions, evaluate information, and make decisions

6. _____ opinion

    c. an idea that may be formed from evidence but has not been confirmed by evidence

Write About It
7. In your notebook, tell how scientific literacy, claims, and reasoning are related.

CHAPTER 1 Review

Read each question and choose the best answer.

---

1 Water is poured into a graduated cylinder. When a rock is dropped into the cylinder, the water level in the cylinder rises.

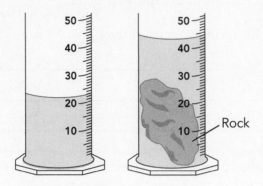

By how much does the water level rise?

A 21 mL

B 23 mL

C 30 mL

D 44 mL

---

2 A student wants to drive the fastest model car for a race. She looks at the previous track times of four available cars.

	Trial 1	Trial 2	Trial 3
Car 1	2.0 s	2.3 s	4.0 s
Car 2	2.5 s	3.0 s	4.5 s
Car 3	4.0 s	4.6 s	8.0 s
Car 4	1.5 s	2.0 s	3.5 s

Which car will she select for the upcoming race?

F Car 1

G Car 2

H Car 3

J Car 4

3 The layers of Earth's interior are shown in the diagram. These layers are the crust, the mantle, and the core. In addition, the model shows two areas called the lithosphere and the asthenosphere, which have their own characteristic properties.

Earth's Interior

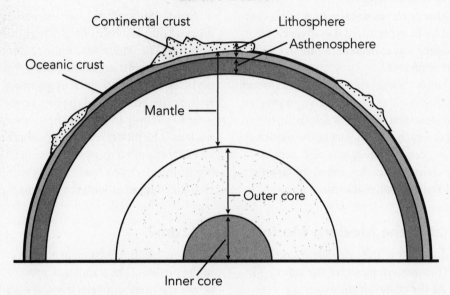

What cannot be determined from this model?

A Relative order of the layers

B Relative thickness of the layers

C Names of the two types of crust

D Thickness of the mantle in kilometers

2.1 Introduction to Atoms

Key Concept Summaries

🔑 How Did Atomic Theory Develop?

The idea of the atom dates back to around 430 B.C. Today, the atom is defined as the smallest particle that can still be considered an element. **Atomic theory grew as a series of models that developed from experimental evidence. As more evidence was collected, the theory and models were revised.**

John Dalton thought that atoms were smooth, hard balls that could not be broken into smaller pieces. He identified other characteristics of atoms, all of which remain part of the modern model. However, J. J. Thomson's discovery of negatively charged particles, called electrons, disproved Dalton's indivisible-atom idea.

Thomson proposed a model in which electrons were scattered throughout a ball of positive charge.

Ernest Rutherford's experiments led him to propose the existence of a nucleus, a small, positively charged region at the center of the atom. Rutherford called the positively charged particles in an atom's nucleus protons. Niels Bohr revised this model to propose that electrons were found only in specific orbits around the nucleus. The modern cloud model proposes that an electron's movement is related to its energy level, and electrons move rapidly within a cloudlike region around the nucleus.

🔑 What Is the Modern Model of the Atom?

With the discovery of the neutrally charged neutron, the modern model of the atom emerged. **At the center of the atom is a tiny, dense nucleus containing protons and neutrons. Surrounding the nucleus is a cloudlike region of moving electrons.** Protons, p+, have a charge of +1 and a mass of 1 amu. Neutrons, n, have no charge and a mass of 1 amu. Electrons, e-, have a charge of –1 and a mass of $\frac{1}{1,840}$ amu.

Almost all the mass of an atom is concentrated in the nucleus. The number of protons, which equals the number of electrons, is called the atomic number. The definition of an element is based on its atomic number. Atoms of an element that have the same number of protons but a different number of neutrons are called isotopes. An isotope is identified by its mass number, which is the sum of the protons and neutrons in the atom.

 **2.1** Introduction to Atoms

Review and Reinforce

Understanding Main Ideas
Answer the following questions in your notebook.

1. What three particles are found in an atom?

2. Which two particles are found in an atom's nucleus?

3. Explain why scientists use models to study atoms.

4. Which two particles in an atom are equal in number?

5. How are elements identified in terms of their atoms?

6. What two particles account for almost all of the mass of an atom?

Building Vocabulary
Fill in the blank to complete each statement.

7. The _____ is the very small, dense center of an atom.

8. The positively charged particle of an atom is called a(n) _____.

9. A particle with no charge is a(n) _____.

10. A(n) _____ is the particle of an atom that moves rapidly in the cloudlike region around the nucleus.

11. The _____ tells the number of protons in the nucleus of every atom of an element.

12. Atoms of the same element that have the same number of protons but different numbers of neutrons are called _____.

13. The sum of protons and neutrons in the nucleus of an atom is the _____.

14. The specific amount of energy an electron has, or its _____, is related to its movement.

✏️ Write About It
15. In your notebook, describe the modern model of the atom.

 **2.2** Organizing the Elements

Key Concept Summaries

What Did Mendeleev Discover?

Dmitri Mendeleev studied the properties of the 63 known elements in an attempt to organize them. He used an element's melting point, density, color, and atomic mass. Atomic mass is the average mass of all of the isotopes of that element. **Mendeleev noticed that a pattern of properties appeared when he arranged the elements in order of increasing atomic mass. He found that the properties repeated regularly.**

Mendeleev called his arrangement of the elements a periodic table because of the repetition of properties. Mendeleev left blank spaces in his table and predicted that these spaces would be filled by elements that had not yet been discovered. He even predicted the properties of those elements. The modern periodic table is arranged according to increasing atomic number.

What Information Does the Periodic Table Contain?

The periodic table contains information for each of the known elements. **In this book, the periodic table includes the atomic number, chemical symbol, name, and atomic mass for each**

element. A chemical symbol is an abbreviation of an element's name. It contains either one or two letters.

How Is the Periodic Table Useful?

The periodic table is made up of rows called periods and columns called groups or families. There are seven periods and 18 groups. **An element's properties can be predicted from its location in the periodic table.** Metals are shown on the left of the table, and nonmetals

are shown on the right. Metalloids are located between the metals and nonmetals. This pattern is repeated in each period and accounts for the fact that elements in the same group have similar properties.

Name _____ Date _____ Class _____

Review and Reinforce

Understanding Main Ideas

The diagram below is a square from the periodic table. Label the four facts shown about each element.

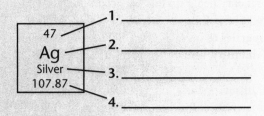

1. _____
2. _____
3. _____
4. _____

Answer the following questions in the spaces provided.

5. In what order did Mendeleev arrange the elements in the periodic table?

_____

6. What do elements in the same column in the periodic table have in common?

_____

7. What can you predict about an element from its position in the periodic table?

_____

Building Vocabulary

Fill in the blank to complete each statement.

8. An element's _____ is its row in the periodic table.

9. The _____ of an element is the average mass of all isotopes of that element.

10. A(n) _____ is an abbreviation for the name of an element and usually has either one or two letters.

Write About It

11. In your notebook, compare and contrast Mendeleev's periodic table with the modern periodic table.

2.3 Metals

Key Concept Summaries

🔑 What Are the Properties of Metals?

The majority of the elements in the periodic table are metals, elements that are good conductors of electric current and heat. The metals begin on the left side of the table and extend most of the way across. **The physical properties of metals include luster, malleability, ductility, and conductivity.**

A material that has a high luster is shiny and reflective. A malleable material can be hammered or rolled into flat sheets. A ductile material can be drawn into long wires. Thermal conductivity is the ability of an object to transfer heat. The ability of an object to carry electric current is electrical conductivity. All of these are physical properties.

The ease and speed with which an element reacts with other substances is called its reactivity. Metals usually react by losing electrons. The deterioration of a metal due to a chemical reaction in the environment is called corrosion. Reactivity and corrosion are chemical properties.

🔑 How Are Metals Classified?

In the periodic table, metals are classified as alkali metals, alkaline earth metals, transition metals, metals in mixed groups, lanthanides, and actinides. The metals in Group 1 are the alkali metals. They are the most reactive metals in the periodic table. They are never found uncombined in nature because they are so reactive. They have low densities and low melting points. Group 2 metals are the alkaline earth metals. They are harder, denser, and melt at higher temperatures than the alkali metals. They are also highly reactive, but not as much so as the alkali metals.

The transition metals are the metals in Groups 3 through 12. Most of these metals are hard and shiny solids with high melting points and high densities. They are less reactive than the Group 1 and 2 metals. Some of the elements in Groups 13 through 16 are metals. The two rows of elements placed below the main part of the periodic table are the lanthanide and actinide metals. Transuranium elements are those that follow uranium and are sometimes called synthetic elements.

2.3 Metals

Review and Reinforce

Understanding Main Ideas

Answer the following questions in the spaces provided. Use a separate sheet of paper if you need more room. Use a periodic table for reference.

1. What physical properties are shared by most metals?

   _____

   _____

2. Sodium (Na) and calcium (Ca) are in different families of metals. Name the families of metals in which they belong, and describe each family's characteristics.

   _____

   _____

3. Would a metal in Group 13 be more or less reactive than a metal in Group 1? Explain.

   _____

4. In what periods are the lanthanides and actinides? Where are they placed in the periodic table? Why?

   _____

   _____

Building Vocabulary

Fill in the blank to complete each statement.

5. The reaction of a metal with oxygen to form rust is called _____.

6. A material that is _____ can be hammered into thin sheets and other shapes.

7. The ability to transmit heat or electricity to other objects is called _____.

8. A material that is _____ can be drawn into a wire.

9. _____ is the ease and speed with which an element combines with other substances.

 **2.4** Nonmetals and Metalloids

Key Concept Summaries

What Are the Properties of Nonmetals?

A nonmetal is an element that lacks most of the properties of a metal. With the exception of hydrogen, nonmetals are found on the right side of the periodic table. Compared to metals, nonmetals have a much wider variety of properties. However, they do have several properties in common. **In general, most nonmetals are poor conductors of electric current and heat. Solid nonmetals tend to be dull and brittle.** Also, nonmetals usually have lower densities than metals.

In terms of chemical properties, atoms of nonmetals usually gain or share electrons when they react with other atoms. Many nonmetals can form compounds with other nonmetals. In these types of compounds, the atoms share their electrons to form bonds. When two or more atoms bond this way, they form a molecule.

What Are the Families Containing Nonmetals?

There are nonmetals in Group 1 and in Groups 14–18. **The families containing nonmetals include the carbon family, the nitrogen family, the oxygen family, the halogen family, the noble gases, and hydrogen.** In Group 14, only carbon is a nonmetal. The nitrogen family contains two nonmetals—nitrogen and phosphorus. In nature, nitrogen is found as a diatomic molecule, or a molecule consisting of two of the same atoms bonded together. The oxygen family contains three nonmetals—oxygen, sulfur, and selenium.

The halogens are the Group 17 nonmetals fluorine, chlorine, bromine, and iodine. All of the halogens are very reactive; fluorine is the most reactive of all the elements. The noble gases are the elements in Group 18. They are usually nonreactive. The chemical properties of hydrogen are very different from those of the other elements, so it cannot be grouped with any family.

Elements that have some properties of metals and some of nonmetals are called metalloids. All metalloids are solid at room temperature, and are brittle, hard, and somewhat reactive. Metalloids such as silicon and germanium are used to make semiconductors, which are substances that can conduct electric current under some conditions but not under others.

2.4 Nonmetals and Metalloids

Review and Reinforce

Understanding Main Ideas

Complete the following table. Use a periodic table for reference.

Element	Metal, Metalloid, or Nonmetal	Family Name
Arsenic	metalloid	**1.**
Sulfur	**2.**	oxygen family
Tin	metal	**3.**
Neon	**4.**	noble gas
Chlorine	nonmetal	**5.**
Silicon	**6.**	carbon family

7. Where in the periodic table are the nonmetals located? Where are the metalloids?

   _____

Building Vocabulary

Fill in the blank to complete each statement.

8. A(n) _____ is formed of two atoms.

9. The _____ are a family of very reactive elements.

10. A type of element that has some of the properties of metals and some of nonmetals is called a(n) _____.

11. The _____ are a family of unreactive elements.

12. A(n) _____ is a type of element whose physical properties are generally opposite to those of metals.

13. A substance that carries electricity under certain circumstances, but not under other circumstances is called a(n) _____.

 ## Write About It

14. In your notebook, describe in your own words the physical and chemical properties of nonmetals.

Name _____ Date _____ Class_____

Read each question and choose the best answer.

---

1 A student knows that copper (Cu) conducts electricity well. Which investigation will help him to confirm that elements in the same group of the periodic table share similar properties?

1 1A																		18 8A
1 H	2 2A											13 3A	14 4A	15 5A	16 6A	17 7A		2 He
3 Li	4 Be											5 B	6 C	7 N	8 O	9 F		10 Ne
11 Na	12 Mg	3 3B	4 4B	5 5B	6 6B	7 7B	8	9 —8B—	10	11 1B	12 2B	13 Al	14 Si	15 P	16 S	17 Cl		18 Ar
19 K	20 Ca	21 Sc	22 Ti	23 V	24 Cr	25 Mn	26 Fe	27 Co	28 Ni	29 Cu	30 Zn	31 Ga	32 Ge	33 As	34 Se	35 Br		36 Kr
37 Rb	38 Sr	39 Y	40 Zr	41 Nb	42 Mo	43 Tc	44 Ru	45 Rh	46 Pd	47 Ag	48 Cd	49 In	50 Sn	51 Sb	52 Te	53 I		54 Xe
55 Cs	56 Ba	71 Lu	72 Hf	73 Ta	74 W	75 Re	76 Os	77 Ir	78 Pt	79 Au	80 Hg	81 Tl	82 Pb	83 Bi	84 Po	85 At		86 Rn
87 Fr	88 Ra	103 Lr	104 Rf	105 Db	106 Sg	107 Bh	108 Hs	109 Mt	110 Ds	111 Rg	112 Cn	113 Uut	114 Fl	115 Uup	116 Lv	117 Uus		118 Uuo

57 La	58 Ce	59 Pr	60 Nd	61 Pm	62 Sm	63 Eu	64 Gd	65 Tb	66 Dy	67 Ho	68 Er	69 Tm	70 Yb
89 Ac	90 Th	91 Pa	92 U	93 Np	94 Pu	95 Am	96 Cm	97 Bk	98 Cf	99 Es	100 Fm	101 Md	102 No

A Compare the conductivity of copper (Cu) with the conductivity of zinc (Zn) and nickel (Ni).

B Mix copper (Cu) with silver (Ag) and test to see whether the mixture conducts electricity.

C Test whether silver (Ag) and gold (Au) conduct electricity well.

D Test whether different isotopes of copper (Cu) conduct electricity.

---

2 William wants to draw a modern model of an atom. Which of the following suggestions would be the most helpful for William in making his drawing?

F The protons should be scattered evenly throughout the atom.

G The nucleus should include protons, neutrons, and electrons.

H The number of neutrons should be equal to the number of protons.

J The electrons should be shown in a cloud surrounding the nucleus.

3 Which information is specified directly by the model of an atom shown below?

20P
20N

A Diameter of the atom

B Identity of the atom

C Speed of the electrons

D Volume of the nucleus

4 The elements sodium and titanium are represented in the periodic table by the images below.

11	22
Na	**Ti**
Sodium	Titanium
22.99	47.90

What can you conclude about sodium and titanium atoms?

F Sodium has more electrons than titanium.

G Titanium atoms have 24.91 more neutrons than sodium atoms.

H Sodium atoms have half as many protons as titanium atoms.

J The average atomic weight of a sodium atom is half the average atomic weight of a titanium atom.

3.1 Atoms, Bonding, and the Periodic Table

Key Concept Summary

What Determines an Element's Chemistry?

An atom's electrons are found in different energy levels. Valence electrons have the highest energy. Each element has a specific number of valence electrons, from 1 to 8. **The number of valence electrons in each atom helps determine the chemical properties of that element.**

An electron dot diagram includes the symbol for an element surrounded by dots. Each dot represents one valence electron. Atoms tend to form bonds so that they have 8 valence electrons and become more stable. Valence electrons may be transferred or shared. A chemical bond is the force of attraction that holds atoms together as a result of the rearrangement of electrons between them.

The periodic table includes rows, called periods, and columns, called groups. The atomic number increases from left to right across each period, as does the number of valence electrons. The first element in each period has 1 valence electron. The last element (except Period 1) has 8 valence electrons. Because elements within a group (except Period 1) have the same number of valence electrons, they have similar properties.

Except for helium, each of the Group 18 elements, the noble gases, has 8 valence electrons. They are stable, unlikely to gain, lose, or share electrons, and do not react easily with other elements. Metal atoms react by losing their valence electrons. A metal's reactivity depends on how easily it loses valence electrons. In general, reactivity decreases from left to right across the periodic table. Nonmetals become stable when their atoms gain or share enough electrons to have 8 valence electrons. Nonmetals usually combine with metals by gaining electrons, but can also combine with other nonmetals and metalloids by sharing. The metalloids, which lie between metals and nonmetals in the periodic table, can either lose or share electrons. They have some properties of both metals and nonmetals.

Hydrogen is placed in Group 1 because it has one valence electron, but it is considered a nonmetal. Its properties differ greatly from the properties of the alkali metals. When it combines with other nonmetals, hydrogen shares its electron and forms a stable arrangement of 2 electrons.

3.1 Atoms, Bonding, and the Periodic Table

Review and Reinforce

Understanding Main Ideas

Look at the diagram below. Then answer the following questions in the space provided.

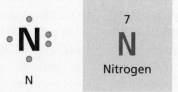

1. How many protons does a nitrogen atom have? _____

2. How many valence electrons does a nitrogen atom have?_____

3. Is nitrogen reactive or stable? _____

4. Neon (Ne), which has an atomic number of 10 is in Group 18 in the periodic table. To which group does nitrogen belong? _____

5. The element directly below nitrogen in the periodic table is phosphorus (P). How many valence electrons does phosphorus have? _____

6. Will the properties of nitrogen be more similar to the properties of neon or the properties of phosphorus? Explain. _____

   _____

   _____

Building Vocabulary

If the statement is true, write *true*. If the statement is false, change the underlined word or words to make the statement true.

7. _____ An element's reactivity is determined by the number of <u>protons</u> found in an atom of the element.

8. _____ The force of attraction that holds two atoms together is called a(n) <u>chemical bond</u>.

9. _____ In a(n) <u>periodic table</u>, dots around an element's symbol indicate the number of valence electrons in an atom.

3.2 Ionic Bonds

Key Concept Summaries

🔑 How Do Ions Form?

An **ion** is an atom or group of atoms that has an electric charge. **When a neutral atom loses a valence electron, it loses a negative charge. It becomes a positive ion. When a neutral atom gains an electron, it gains a negative charge. It becomes a negative ion.** Metal atoms are likely to lose electrons. They lose electrons in order to have a stable arrangement of 8 valence electrons at a lower energy level.

Ions that are made of more than 1 atom are called **polyatomic ions.** Like other ions, polyatomic ions have an overall positive or negative charge. When atoms that easily lose electrons react with atoms that easily gain electrons, valence electrons are transferred from one type of atom to another. The transfer gives each type of atom a more stable arrangement of electrons. An **ionic bond** is the attraction between two oppositely charged ions. The resulting compound is called an **ionic compound.** It is made up of positive and negative ions.

🔑 How Are the Formulas and Names of Ionic Compounds Written?

A **chemical formula** is a group of symbols that shows the ratio of elements in a compound. For example, the formula for sodium chloride is NaCl. **Subscripts** tell the ratio of elements in a compound. For example, in H_2O, there are two hydrogen atoms and one oxygen atom, so the ratio is 2 to 1. **To write the formula for an ionic compound, write the symbol of the positive ion and then the symbol of the negative ion. Add the subscripts that are needed to balance the charges. For an ionic compound, the name of the positive ion comes first, followed by the name of the negative ion.**

🔑 What Are Properties of Ionic Compounds?

In general, ionic compounds form hard, brittle crystals that have high melting points. They conduct electric current when dissolved in water or melted. Ionic compounds form solids by building up repeating patterns of ions. The ions form an orderly, three-dimensional arrangement called a **crystal.** Many crystals of ionic compounds are hard and brittle. This is due to the strength of their ionic bonds and the attractions among all the ions. It takes a huge amount of energy to separate the ions in a crystal. As a result, ionic compounds have very high melting points.

Electric current is the flow of charged particles. When ionic crystals dissolve in water, the ions are free to move about, and the solution can conduct current. Likewise, when an ionic compound melts, the ions are able to move freely, and the liquid conducts current. In contrast, ionic compounds in solid form do not conduct current well.

3.2 Ionic Bonds

Review and Reinforce

Understanding Main Ideas

Fill in the blank to complete each statement.

1. Negative ions form when atoms _____ valence electrons.

2. In the formation of an ionic compound, a metal atom is most likely to _____ valence electrons.

3. Ionic compounds form because _____ charges attract.

4. An ionic solution can conduct _____.

Answer the following questions in the spaces provided. You may use a periodic table.

5. A potassium ion has a charge of 1+. A sulfide ion has a charge of 2–. What is the chemical formula for potassium sulfide?

   _____

6. Name the following compound: MgO.

   _____

7. Describe the electrical conductivity of a solid ionic compound.

   _____

Building Vocabulary

Write a definition for each of these terms in your notebook.

8. ion

9. polyatomic ion

10. ionic bond

11. ionic compound

12. chemical formula

3.3 Covalent Bonds

Key Concept Summaries

⬤ How Are Atoms Held Together in a Covalent Bond?

Two atoms can form a bond by sharing electrons. The chemical bond formed when two atoms share electrons is called a covalent bond. Covalent bonds usually form between nonmetal atoms. **The attractions between the shared electrons and the protons in the nucleus of each atom hold the atoms together in a covalent bond.** The two bonded atoms form a molecule. A molecule is a neutral group of atoms joined by covalent bonds. If two atoms share *two* pairs of electrons, the bond is called a double bond. If the two atoms share *three* pairs of electrons, the bond is called a triple bond. A molecule can include more than two atoms and therefore a number of different bonds.

⬤ What Are Properties of Molecular Compounds?

A molecular compound is a compound that is composed of molecules. The molecules of a molecular compound contain atoms that are covalently bonded. **Unlike ionic compounds, molecular compounds usually do not conduct electric current when melted or dissolved in water. Also, compared to ionic compounds, molecular compounds generally have lower melting points and boiling points.** There are no charged particles available to move in molecular compounds, so they don't carry current well. In molecular solids, forces hold the molecules close to one another. But the forces between molecules are much weaker than the forces between ions. That's why the melting points and boiling points of molecular solids are generally much lower than those of ionic solids.

⬤ How Do Bonded Atoms Become Partially Charged?

Unequal sharing of electrons causes covalently bonded atoms to have slight electric charges. A covalent bond in which electrons are shared equally, such as H_2, is a nonpolar bond. When electrons in a covalent bond are shared unequally, a polar bond is formed. Hydrogen fluoride, HF, has a polar bond. Polar bonds can create polar molecules—molecules that have positively charged ends and negatively charged ends. The properties of polar and nonpolar compounds are different because of differences in attractions between their molecules. The attractions between polar molecules require more energy to overcome than the attractions between nonpolar molecules.

3.3 Covalent Bonds

Review and Reinforce

Understanding Main Ideas

Answer the following questions in the spaces provided.
Use the diagram to the right to answer questions 1–5.

(+) H:F: (−)   :O::O:

:N:::N: :F:F:

1. Circle all of the covalent bonds in the electron dot diagrams.

2. Which bond(s) shown are double bonds?

    _____

3. Which bond(s) shown are triple bonds?

    _____

4. Which molecule(s) shown have polar bonds?

    _____

5. Compare and contrast O_2 and F_2.

    _____

    _____

Building Vocabulary

Match each term with its definition by writing the letter of the correct definition in the right column on the line beside the term in the left column.

6. _____ molecule

7. _____ double bond

8. _____ nonpolar bond

9. _____ polar bond

10. _____ covalent bond

a. the chemical bond formed when two atoms share electrons

b. a neutral group of atoms joined by covalent bonds

c. a bond in which electrons are shared unequally

d. a bond in which electrons are shared equally

e. a bond in which four electrons are shared

Write About It

11. In your notebook, compare and contrast carbon dioxide and water, including the types of bonds involved and the properties of the compounds.

3.4 Observing Chemical Change

Key Concept Summaries

🔑 How Can Changes in Matter Be Described?

Matter is often described by its characteristic properties, which are physical or chemical attributes that are unique to a particular substance.

A physical property is a characteristic of a substance that can be observed without changing the substance into another substance. The temperature for melting a solid is a physical property. Color, texture, density, and conductivity are physical properties of matter. A chemical property is a characteristic of a substance that describes its ability to change into another substance. To observe the chemical properties of a substance, it must change or be changed into another substance. A chemical property can be a material's flammability or its ability to rust or tarnish.

Changes in matter can be described in terms of physical changes and chemical changes. A physical change is any change that alters the form or appearance of the substance but does not change it into another substance. A change in matter that produces one or more new substances is a chemical change, or chemical reaction. In a chemical change, the atoms rearrange to form new substances. When a substance undergoes a chemical change, it results in different physical properties as well. Substances that undergo chemical changes are called reactants. The new substances that form are the products. Chemical changes occur when existing bonds break and new bonds form. New substances are produced.

🔑 How Do You Identify a Chemical Reaction?

Chemical reactions involve changes in properties and changes in energy that you can often observe. One way to detect chemical reactions is to observe changes in physical properties of materials. For instance, formation of a precipitate, gas production, and a color change are possible evidence that a chemical reaction has taken place. A precipitate is a solid that forms from liquids during a chemical reaction, such as the curds that form in souring milk. But the only sure evidence of a chemical reaction is that one or more new substances are produced.

A chemical reaction occurs when bonds break and new bonds form. Breaking bonds requires energy, while forming bonds releases energy. In an exothermic reaction, energy released as the products form is greater than the energy required to break the bonds of the reactants. The energy is usually released as heat. In an endothermic reaction, more energy is required to break the bonds of the reactants than is released by the formation of the products. When energy is absorbed, the surroundings become cooler.

3.4 Observing Chemical Change

Review and Reinforce

Understanding Main Ideas

Complete the following table. Describe changes in properties that you might notice during each process and state whether the changes are chemical or physical.

Changes in Matter		
Event	Observable Changes	Type of Change
Baking a cake	1.	2.
Burning a log	3.	4.
Freezing water	5.	6.

Building Vocabulary

Fill in the blank to complete each statement.

7. Any change that alters a substance without changing it into another substance is a(n) _____ change.

8. _____ is anything that has mass and takes up space.

9. A reaction that releases energy in the form of heat is called a(n) _____ reaction.

10. A(n) _____ reaction is a reaction in which energy is absorbed.

11. A chemical change is also referred to as a(n) _____.

12. A(n) _____ is a solid formed from liquid reactants during a chemical reaction.

 ## Write About It

13. In your notebook, describe what happens when reactants form products.

3.5 Describing Chemical Reactions

Key Concept Summaries

What Information Does a Chemical Equation Contain?

A chemical equation is a way to show a chemical reaction, using symbols instead of words. The formula of a compound identifies the elements in the compound and the ratio in which the atoms or ions are present. **A chemical equation tells you the substances you start with** (reactants) **in a reaction and the substances that are formed** at the end (products). The formulas for the reactants are written on the left, followed by an arrow, which is read as "yields." The formulas for the products are written to the right of the arrow. Plus signs are used to separate two or more reactants or products.

How Is Mass Conserved During a Chemical Reaction?

The law of conservation of mass states that during a chemical reaction, matter is not created or destroyed. **In a chemical reaction, all of the atoms present at the start of the reaction are present at the end of the reaction.** According to the law of conservation of mass, the total mass is the same before and after the reaction.

Some reactions may seem to violate the principle of conservation of mass. In an open system, matter can enter from or escape to the surroundings. A closed system is required to ensure that matter does not enter or leave.

The law of conservation of mass means that to be accurate, a chemical equation must show the same number of atoms of each element on both sides of the equation. An equation is balanced when conservation of mass is correctly shown. Coefficients are often used to balance chemical equations. A coefficient is a number placed in front of a chemical formula in an equation. It tells you the amount of a reactant or a product that takes part in a reaction.

What Are Three Types of Chemical Reactions?

Three types of chemical reactions are synthesis, decomposition, and replacement. In a synthesis reaction, two or more elements or compounds combine to form a more complex substance. A decomposition reaction occurs when compounds break down into simpler products. In a replacement reaction, one element replaces another element in a compound (single replacement) or two elements in different compounds trade places (double replacement).

3.5 Describing Chemical Reactions

Review and Reinforce

Understanding Main Ideas

Complete the table. Balance each equation. Then indicate whether the reaction is a synthesis, decomposition, or replacement reaction.

Given Equation	Balanced Equation	Type of Reaction
$FeS + HCl \rightarrow FeCl_2 + H_2S$	1.	2.
$Na + F_2 \rightarrow NaF$	3.	4.
$HgO \rightarrow Hg + O_2$	5.	6.

Answer questions 7 and 8 in your notebook.

7. Describe in words the reaction represented by the equation and include a description of the composition of each kind of molecule.
$2 H_2 + O_2 \rightarrow 2 H_2O$

8. Use the law of conservation of mass to explain why the equation in question 7 is balanced.

Building Vocabulary

Match each term with its definition by writing the letter of the correct definition in the right column on the line beside the term in the left column.

9. _____ chemical equation

10. _____ decomposition reaction

11. _____ coefficient

12. _____ product

13. _____ reactant

14. _____ synthesis reaction

15. _____ replacement reaction

16. _____ conservation of mass

a. substance present after a reaction

b. reaction in which substances combine to form a more complex compound

c. law that states that matter is not created or destroyed during a chemical reaction

d. reaction in which one element replaces another in a compound

e. substance present before a reaction

f. number telling how many molecules of a substance are involved in a chemical reaction

g. reaction in which compounds are broken down into simpler substances

h. uses symbols and formulas to show chemical reactions

CHAPTER **3** **Review**

Read each question and choose the best answer.

1 Look at the model of fluorine.

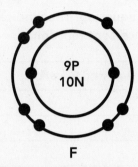

9P
10N

F

Which change would make fluorine less reactive?

A Add a proton to the nucleus.

B Add a neutron to the nucleus.

C Add an electron to the lower energy level.

D Add an electron to the higher energy level.

2 The formula for cupric nitrate is shown below.

$$Cu(NO_3)_2$$

What atoms are found in one formula unit of cupric nitrate?

F 1 atom of copper, 1 atom of nitrogen, and 3 atoms of oxygen

G 2 atoms of copper, 1 atom of nitrogen, and 3 atoms of oxygen

H 1 atom of copper, 2 atoms of nitrogen, and 6 atoms of oxygen

J 2 atoms of copper, 2 atoms of nitrogen, and 6 atoms of oxygen

3 Look at the model and chemical equation for the formation of a water molecule.

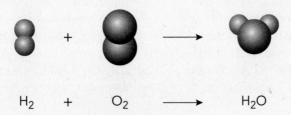

$$H_2 \quad + \quad O_2 \quad \longrightarrow \quad H_2O$$

What is wrong with the equation?

A It does not correspond with the model above it.

B It contains two reactants but only one product.

C It does not show that mass is conserved in the reaction.

D It does not indicate the number of atoms in the reactants and product.

4 A change in which of the following properties is most likely to indicate a chemical change?

F Color

G Phase

H Shape

J Size

4.1 Motion, Speed, and Velocity

Key Concept Summaries

🔑 How Does Speed Describe Motion?

Speed is a measurement that describes the distance a moving object travels per unit of time. The SI unit for speed is meters per second (m/s). Speed can be described in two ways. Instantaneous speed is the speed of an object at one instant of time. Instantaneous speed is useful for describing the motion of an object that slows down or speeds up during a trip. Average speed is the overall rate of speed at which an object moves. Average speed can be calculated by dividing the total distance traveled by the total amount of time taken for that travel.

🔑 How Does Velocity Describe Motion?

Speed is not the only measure of motion. Scientists often used velocity to more fully describe the motion of an object. Velocity describes both an object's speed and the direction of its motion. Because velocity includes both speed and direction, the velocity of an object can change even if the speed of the object stays the same. For example, two cars may be traveling at the same speed of 16 m/s. However, one may have a velocity of 16 m/s west, while the other has a different velocity of 16 m/s east.

🔑 How Can Motion Be Graphed?

Graphs can be used to compare the motion of different objects. **You can use a line graph that plots an object's distance versus its time to describe the object's motion.** On a distance-versus-time graph, the horizontal axis, or x-axis, shows time. The vertical axis, or y-axis, shows distance. Each point on the graph represents the distance an object has traveled by a certain amount of time.

Slope is the steepness of a line on a graph. The slope of the line shows you how fast the variable on the x-axis is changing in relation to the variable on the y-axis. On a distance-versus-time graph, the slope represents speed. A steeper slope represents a faster speed than a slope that is less steep. A straight graph line represents motion with a constant speed.

You can calculate slope by dividing the rise by the run. The rise is the vertical distance between two points on the line. The run is the horizontal distance between these same two points.

Name _____ Date _____ Class _____

4.1 Motion, Speed, and Velocity

Review and Reinforce

Understanding Main Ideas
Fill in the blank to complete each statement.

1. To find the average speed of a ship traveling between two ports, divide the distance between ports by the ship's _____ travel time.

2. A speedometer on a car shows you _____ speed.

3. The velocity of a train traveling 33,300 meters west in 30 minutes is 18.5 _____.

4. You can calculate the slope of a line by dividing its rise by its _____.

5. Two airplanes traveling at the same speed have a different velocity if they are traveling in different _____.

Building Vocabulary
In your notebook, write a definition for each of these terms.

6. slope
7. velocity
8. instantaneous speed
9. speed
10. average speed

Write About It
11. In your notebook, explain why the line with the steepest slope on a distance-versus-time graph could represent the fastest car in a car race.

4.2 Acceleration

Key Concept Summaries

🔑 What Is Acceleration?

In everyday language, acceleration means "the process of speeding up." Scientists define acceleration as the rate at which velocity changes. **In science, acceleration refers to increasing speed, decreasing speed, or changing direction.** Whenever an object's speed changes, the object accelerates. The change in speed can be either to speed up or to slow down. Slowing down is sometimes called deceleration, or negative acceleration. Even an object moving at constant speed can be accelerating—as long as it is changing direction.

Acceleration describes the rate at which velocity changes. If an object is not changing direction, you can describe its acceleration as the rate at which its speed changes. To determine the acceleration of an object moving in a straight line, use the following equation.

$$\text{Acceleration} = \frac{\text{(Final Speed – Initial Speed)}}{\text{Time}}$$

If speed is measured in meters per second (m/s) and time is measured in seconds, the SI unit of acceleration is meters per second per second, or m/s^2.

🔑 How Do You Graph Acceleration?

You can use both a speed-versus-time graph and a distance-versus-time graph to analyze the motion of an accelerating object. The slope of the speed-versus-time graph is the acceleration. A slanted straight line on a speed-versus-time graph means that the acceleration of the object is constant, but not zero. If the line slants upward, speed was increasing. If the line slopes downward, speed was decreasing.

On a distance-versus-time graph, an upward increasing curved line indicates that the speed is increasing. Acceleration is occurring.

Name _____ Date _____ Class _____

4.2 Acceleration

Review and Reinforce

Understanding Main Ideas
Answer the following questions in the spaces provided.

1. In science, what three changes can each cause an object to accelerate?

   _____

2. What is the equation for finding the acceleration of an object moving in a straight line?

   _____

3. Graph A below plots a race car's speed for 5 seconds. What is the car's rate of acceleration?

   _____

4. Graph B below plots the same race car's speed for a different 5-second interval. What is the car's rate of acceleration during this interval?

   _____

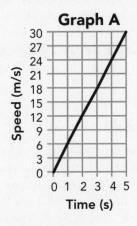
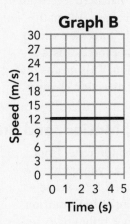

Building Vocabulary
Write a definition for the term on the lines below.

5. acceleration

   _____

   _____

Name _____ Date _____ Class _____

Key Concept Summaries

🔑 How Are Forces Described?

A **force** is a push or a pull. When one object pushes or pulls another object, the first object exerts a force on the second object. You exert a force on a chair when you pull it away from a table.

Like velocity and acceleration, a force is described by its strength and by the direction in which it acts. Pushing to the left is a different force from pushing to the right. The direction and strength of a force can be represented by an arrow. The arrow points in the direction of the force. The length of the arrow tells you the strength of the force—the longer the arrow, the greater the force. The strength of a force is measured in an SI unit called the **newton** (N).

🔑 How Do Forces Affect Motion?

Often more than one force acts on an object at the same time. The combination of all the forces acting on an object is called the **net force.** It determines if and how an object will accelerate.

You can find the net force on an object by adding together the strengths of all the individual forces on the object. When the total is 0, the forces are balanced. Balanced forces do not change the motion of an object. When the total is a nonzero number, the forces are said to be unbalanced. **A nonzero net force causes a change in the object's motion. This means that either the object's speed or direction changes.**

When forces on an object act in opposite directions, you find the strength of the net force by subtracting the strength of the smaller force from the strength of the larger force. When forces act in opposite directions, the net force is in the same direction as the larger force.

When a net force acts on an object, the forces are said to be **unbalanced forces.** Unbalanced forces acting on an object will change the object's acceleration. Equal forces acting on an object in opposite directions are called **balanced forces.** Balanced forces do not change an object's motion.

🔑 How Are Force, Motion, and Energy Related?

You know that changes in motion result from unbalanced forces. But how can you apply a force that can unbalance other forces? **In order to apply a force that changes an object's motion, energy must be used. Energy** is the ability to cause change or do work. The two basic types of energy are potential energy and kinetic energy. **Potential energy** is stored energy, resulting from an object's position. Energy that results from the motion of an object is called **kinetic energy.**

4.3 The Nature of Force

Review and Reinforce

Understanding Main Ideas

In the Venn diagram, write the phrases listed below to describe unbalanced forces and balanced forces. Write the characteristics shared by unbalanced and balanced forces in the area of overlap.

1.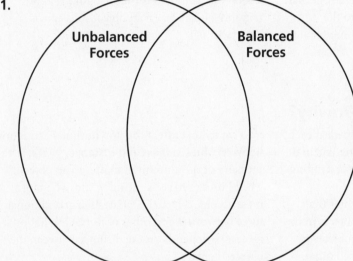

change an object's motion

have direction

net force = 0 N

push or pull

do not change an object's motion

net force does not equal 0 N

Building Vocabulary

Match each term with its definition by writing the letter of the correct definition in the right column on the line beside the term in the left column.

2. _____ newton   a. the SI unit for force

3. _____ force   b. sum of all forces acting on an object

4. _____ balanced forces   c. push or pull

5. _____ unbalanced forces d. can change an object's motion

6. _____ net force   e. will not change an object's motion

Write About It

7. You push on one side of an open door with a force of 120 N. Your friend pushes on the other side of the door with an equal force. In your notebook, explain how these two forces affect the motion of the door.

4.4 Friction and Gravity

Key Concept Summaries

🔑 What Factors Affect Friction?

The force that two surfaces exert on each other when they rub against each other is called **friction. Two factors that affect the force of friction are the types of surfaces involved and how hard the surfaces are pushed together.** Friction acts in a direction opposite to the direction of the object's motion. Without friction, a moving object will not stop until it strikes another object.

There are four types of friction. **Sliding friction** occurs when two solid surfaces slide over each other. **Static friction** acts between objects that aren't moving. **Fluid friction** occurs when a solid object moves through a fluid. **Rolling friction** occurs when an object rolls across a surface.

🔑 What Factors Affect Gravity?

Gravity is a force that pulls objects toward each other. Gravity keeps the moon orbiting Earth. It keeps all the planets in our solar system orbiting the sun.

The law of universal gravitation states that the force of gravity acts between all objects in the universe that have mass. So, any two objects in the universe that have mass attract each other. You are attracted not only to Earth but also to the moon, the other planets in the solar system, and all the objects around you. Earth and the objects around you are attracted to you as well. However, you do not notice the attraction among small objects because these forces are extremely small compared to the force of Earth's attraction.

Two factors affect the gravitational attraction between objects: mass and distance. Mass is a measure of the amount of matter in an object. The SI unit of mass is the kilogram. The more mass an object has, the greater the gravitational force between it and other objects. Gravitational force also depends on the distance between the objects' centers.

Mass is sometimes confused with weight. **Weight** is a measure of the force of gravity on an object. Mass is a measure of the amount of matter in an object. At any given time, your mass is the same on Earth as it would be on any other planet. But your weight would vary on each planet, since the strength of each planet's gravitational force is different.

4.4 Friction and Gravity

Review and Reinforce

Understanding Main Ideas
Answer the following questions in the spaces provided.

1. What are the two factors that affect the frictional force between two surfaces?

   _____

2. What two factors affect the gravitational force between two objects?

   _____

3. How does mass differ from weight? _____

   _____

   _____

Building Vocabulary
Match each term with its definition by writing the letter of the correct definition in the right column on the line beside the term in the left column.

4. _____ friction

5. _____ rolling friction

6. _____ sliding friction

7. _____ fluid friction

8. _____ static friction

9. _____ weight

10. _____ gravity

a. the force that pulls objects toward each other

b. the type of friction that exists between oil and a door hinge

c. the force that one surface exerts on another when two surfaces rub against each other

d. the type of friction that occurs when you rub sandpaper against wood

e. the type of friction that occurs when a wheel turns on a surface

f. a measure of the force of gravity on an object

g. the type of friction that occurs between objects that aren't moving

4.5 Newton's Laws of Motion

Key Concept Summaries

⊂⊃ What Is Newton's First Law of Motion?

If an object is not moving, it will not start moving until a force acts on it. If an object is moving, it will continue at a constant velocity until a force acts to change its speed or direction. **Newton's first law of motion states that an object at rest will remain at rest unless acted upon by a nonzero net force. An object moving at a constant velocity will continue moving at a constant velocity unless acted upon by a nonzero net force.**

All objects resist changes in motion. Resistance to change in motion is called inertia. The greater the mass of an object, the greater its inertia, and the greater the force required to change its motion.

⊂⊃ What Is Newton's Second Law of Motion?

Newton's second law of motion states that an object's acceleration depends on its mass and on the net force acting on it. This relationship can be written as:

$$\text{Acceleration} = \frac{\text{Net force}}{\text{Mass}}$$

The formula can be rearranged to show how much force must be applied to an object to get it to accelerate at a certain rate.

$$\text{Net force} = \text{Mass} \times \text{Acceleration}$$

Acceleration is measured in meters per second per second (m/s^2). Mass is measured in kilograms (kg). Newton's second law shows that force is measured in kilograms times meters per second per second ($kg \cdot m/s^2$). This unit is also called the newton (N), which is the SI unit of force.

⊂⊃ What Is Newton's Third Law of Motion?

Newton's third law of motion states that if one object exerts a force on another object, then the second object exerts a force of equal strength in the opposite direction on the first object.

Another way to state Newton's third law is that for every action there is an equal but opposite reaction.

Pairs of action and reaction forces are all around you. Action and reaction forces do not necessarily cancel out because they may act on different objects.

4.5 Newton's Laws of Motion

Review and Reinforce

Understanding Main Ideas

Answer the following questions in the spaces provided. Use your notebook if you need more room.

1. Newton's second law of motion describes the relationship among force, mass, and acceleration. Write the equation.

   _____

2. How does the diagram at the right illustrate Newton's third law of motion?

   _____

   _____

   _____

If the statement is true, write *true*. If the statement is false, change the underlined word or words to make the statement true.

3. _____ If you increase the force on an object, its acceleration <u>increases</u>.

4. _____ If you increase the mass of an object, its acceleration <u>decreases</u>.

5. _____ To accelerate a 3 kg skateboard at 9 m/s^2, a force of <u>3 newtons</u> is needed.

6. _____ The amount of inertia an object has depends on its <u>speed</u>.

Building Vocabulary

Write a definition for the term on the lines below.

7. inertia

   _____

   _____

CHAPTER 4 Review

Read each question and choose the best answer.

---

1 Kathy goes for a jog. Two minutes later, Rachel also sets out for a jog. The distance that they travel is plotted for 10 minutes.

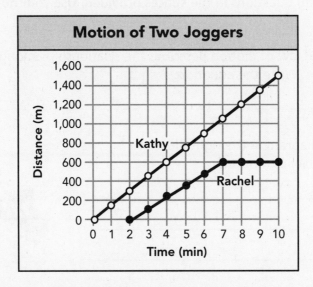

What can you conclude about Kathy and Rachel's motion?

A Kathy's speed increases at a constant rate for 10 minutes.

B Rachel accelerates from 2 minutes to 7 minutes, then jogs at a constant speed.

C Rachel jogs with an average speed of 120 meters/minute for her first 5 minutes.

D If Kathy continues at the same pace, she will jog 2,400 meters in 20 minutes.

---

2 An object at rest experiences a 15 N force to the right and a 25 N force to the left.

What is the net force, and how will the force affect the object?

F 35 N; The object will move to the right.

G 10 N; The object will move to the right.

H 35 N; The object will move to the left.

J 10 N; The object will move to the left.

3 A spring scale is used to pull a block across the surface of an ice rink.

Block

5 4 3 2 1 0 N

If the block has a mass of 7.0 kg, what is the acceleration of the block in meters per second?

---

4 A student states that the velocity of a train is 95 kilometers per hour. What is wrong with this statement?

F Velocity must include both a speed and a direction.

G Velocity is a measure of the change in speed over time.

H Velocity must be expressed in units of kilometers per hour squared.

J Velocity is the distance that an object travels in one second, not one hour.

5.1 Earth in Space

Key Concept Summaries

🗝 How Does Earth Move?

Earth moves in space in two major ways: rotation and revolution. Rotation is the spinning of Earth on its axis. Earth's axis is an imaginary line that passes through Earth's center and the North and South poles. The rotation of Earth causes day and night.

Revolution is the movement of one object around another. One revolution of Earth around the sun is one year. Earth's path, or orbit, around the sun is an ellipse. The ellipse brings the planet closest to the sun in January.

People of many cultures have used the motions of Earth and the moon to establish calendars. A calendar is a system of organizing time that defines the beginning, length, and divisions of a year.

🗝 What Causes Seasons?

Near the equator, sunlight hits Earth's surface from almost overhead. Near the poles, sunlight arrives at a steep angle. As a result, near the poles sunlight is spread out over a greater area. That's why it is warmer near the equator than near the poles.

If Earth's axis were straight up and down relative to its orbit, temperatures in an area would remain fairly constant year-round. There would be no seasons. However, Earth's axis is tilted at an angle of 23.5˚ from the vertical. So as Earth revolves around the sun, the north end of its axis is tilted away from the sun for part of the year and toward the sun for part of the year. **Earth has seasons because its axis is tilted as it revolves around the sun.**

The sun appears farthest north or south of the equator twice each year. Each of these days is called a solstice. In the Northern Hemisphere, the summer solstice occurs around June 21. That is the longest day of the year in the Northern Hemisphere and the shortest day in the Southern Hemisphere. Similarly, around December 21, the winter solstice occurs in the Northern Hemisphere, while the summer solstice occurs in the Southern Hemisphere. Halfway between the solstices, neither hemisphere is tilted toward the sun. Each of these days is called an equinox. On an equinox, the noon sun is directly overhead at the equator, rises due east, and sets due west.

Review and Reinforce

Understanding Main Ideas

Use the diagram below to answer Questions 1–3 in your notebook.

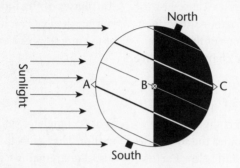

1. In the diagram, what season is it in North America?

2. Would a person at each of the points A, B, and C see the sun? If so, where would the sun be in the sky?

3. Which is a person standing at point B seeing, sunrise or sunset? Explain.

Building Vocabulary

Match each term with its definition by writing the letter of the correct definition in the right column on the line beside the term in the left column.

4. _____ axis   a. path of Earth as it revolves around the sun

5. _____ rotation   b. defines the beginning, length, and divisions of a year

6. _____ revolution   c. line passing through Earth's center and poles

7. _____ orbit   d. when the sun is farthest north or south of the equator

8. _____ calendar   e. movement of Earth around the sun

9. _____ equinox   f. movement of Earth around its axis

10. _____ solstice   g. when the noon sun is directly overhead at the equator

 ## Write About It

11. In your notebook, identify the two major ways Earth moves in space. Then, explain how the tilt of Earth's axis affects the seasons.

5.2 Phases and Eclipses

Key Concept Summaries

What Causes the Moon's Phases?

The different shapes of the moon you see from Earth are called phases. Phases are caused by the motions of the moon around Earth. As the moon orbits Earth, the relative positions of the moon, Earth, and the sun change. **The changing relative positions of the moon, Earth, and the sun cause the phases of the moon.** The phase of the moon you see depends on how much of the sunlit side of the moon faces Earth.

What Are Eclipses?

The moon's orbit around Earth is slightly tilted with respect to Earth's orbit around the sun. As a result, the moon travels above and below Earth's orbit. But on rare occasions, Earth, the moon, and the sun line up.

When an object in space comes between the sun and a third object, it casts a shadow on that third object, causing an eclipse to take place. There are two types of eclipses: solar eclipses and lunar eclipses.

A solar eclipse occurs when the moon passes directly between Earth and the sun, blocking sunlight from Earth. The moon's shadow then hits Earth.

The moon's shadow has two parts. The darker part is the umbra. The larger, lighter part is the penumbra. During a solar eclipse, the sun's light is completely blocked to people within the umbra. They see a total solar eclipse. Part of the sun's light remains visible in the penumbra. So people within the penumbra see a partial solar eclipse.

A lunar eclipse occurs at a full moon when Earth is directly between the moon and the sun. **During a lunar eclipse, Earth blocks sunlight from reaching the moon.** Lunar eclipses occur only when there is a full moon because the moon is closest to Earth at that time.

Earth's shadow also has an umbra and penumbra. When the moon is in Earth's umbra, you see a total lunar eclipse. For most lunar eclipses, Earth, the moon, and the sun are not quite in line, and only a partial lunar eclipse occurs.

5.2 Phases and Eclipses

Review and Reinforce

Understanding Main Ideas

Use the diagram below to answer Question 1 in the spaces provided.

1. What phase of the moon would someone on Earth see when the moon is at positions A through F?

   A: _____

   B: _____

   C: _____

   D: _____

   E: _____

   F: _____

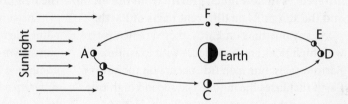

Building Vocabulary

Fill in the blank to complete each statement.

2. A(n) _____ occurs when the moon's shadow hits Earth or Earth's shadow hits the moon.

3. A person standing in the moon's _____ would see a partial solar eclipse.

4. A person standing in the moon's _____ would see a total solar eclipse.

5. The _____ of the moon you see depends on how much of the sunlit side of the moon faces Earth.

6. A(n) _____ eclipse occurs at a full moon when Earth is directly between the moon and the sun.

7. A(n) _____ occurs when the moon passes between Earth and the sun.

Write About It

8. In your notebook, explain how interactions of the moon, Earth, and the sun cause the phases of the moon and eclipses.

5.3 Tides

Key Concept Summary

🗝 What Are Tides?

The force of gravity pulls the moon and Earth (including the water on Earth's surface) toward each other. As a result, **tides,** the rise and fall of ocean water, occur approximately every 12.5 hours. **Tides are caused mainly by differences in how much gravity from the moon and the sun pulls on different parts of Earth.**

At any one time on Earth, there are two places with high tides and two places with low tides. As Earth rotates, one high tide occurs on the side of Earth that faces the moon. The second high tide occurs on the opposite side of Earth. Halfway between the high tides, water flows toward the high tides, causing low tides.

The moon's gravity pulls a little more strongly on the water on the side of Earth closest to the moon than on Earth as a whole. This difference causes a bulge of water on the side of Earth closest to the moon. The bulge causes high tide.

The moon's gravity pulls more weakly on the water on the far side of Earth than on Earth as a whole. Since Earth is pulled more strongly, the water is "left behind." Water flows toward the far side, causing high tide.

The sun is so massive that, even though it is about 150 million kilometers from Earth, its gravity also affects the tides. The sun pulls the water on Earth's surface toward it. **Changes in the positions of Earth, the moon, and the sun affect the heights of the tides during a month.**

The sun, the moon, and Earth are nearly in a line during a new moon. The gravity of the sun and moon pull in the same direction. Their combined forces produce a tide with the greatest difference between consecutive low and high tides, called a **spring tide.**

During the moon's first-quarter phase, the line between Earth and the sun is at right angles to the line between Earth and the moon. The sun's pull is at right angles to the moon's pull. This arrangement produces a **neap tide,** a tide with the least difference between consecutive low and high tides. Neap tides occur twice a month.

At full moon, the moon and the sun are on opposite side of Earth. Since there are high tides on both sides of Earth, a spring tide is also produced. It doesn't matter in which order the sun, Earth, and the moon line up.

Tides

Review and Reinforce

Understanding Main Ideas

Use the diagram at right to answer Question 1 in the spaces provided.

1. What kind of tide will occur when the moon is at positions A, C, D, and F?

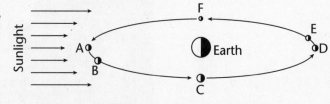

_____

_____

_____

Building Vocabulary

Fill in the blank to complete each statement.

2. A(n) _____ tide occurs when the sun is at right angles to the line between Earth and the moon.

3. Differences in the moon's and sun's pull on different sides of Earth cause _____.

4. A(n) _____ tide occurs when the sun, Earth and the moon are nearly in a line.

5. _____ pulls all objects in the universe, including the moon and Earth and the sun and Earth, toward each other.

6. The term _____ comes from an Old English word, *springen,* meaning "to jump."

Write About It

7. In your notebook, draw two diagrams showing the relative positions of Earth, the sun, and the moon during a spring tide. Show the phase of the moon in each diagram.

Name _____ Date _____ Class _____

CHAPTER 5 Review

Read each question and choose the best answer.

1 At which location in Earth's rotation is it summer in the Northern Hemisphere?

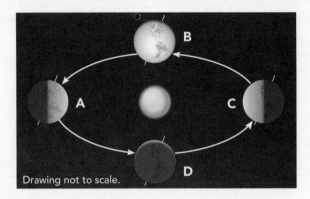

Drawing not to scale.

A Location A

B Location B

C Location C

D Location D

2 Which of the following best explains why observers on Earth will see different phases of the moon during its orbit around Earth?

F The moon radiates different fractions of light throughout its orbit.

G As the moon orbits around Earth, it passes in and out of Earth's shadow.

H The amount of the moon's sunlit surface that can be seen from Earth changes throughout its orbit.

J The rotation of Earth on its axis obstructs different parts of the moon from various locations on Earth.

3 For one week an astronomer watches the moon. She observes the following sequence of phases: first quarter moon, waxing gibbous moon, and full moon. Which phase would the astronomer expect to observe next?

A

B

C

D

4 A scientist observes that the height of the high tide at the Bay of Fundy is at a monthly low. What can she conclude about the angle formed by Earth, the sun, and the moon at this time?

F They form a 0° angle.

G They form a 45° angle.

H They form a 90° angle.

J They form a 180° angle.

6.1 Telescopes

Key Concept Summaries

What Are the Regions of the Electromagnetic Spectrum?

Electromagnetic radiation is energy that can travel through space in the form of waves. Visible light, the light you can see, is just one of many types of electromagnetic radiation. Many objects give off radiation that you cannot see.

The distance between the crest of one wave and the crest of the next wave is called the wavelength. Visible light has very short wavelengths, less than one millionth of a meter.

Other types of radiation have much longer wavelengths, even several meters long. If you shine white light through a prism, the light spreads out to make a range of different colors with different wavelengths, called a spectrum. **The electromagnetic spectrum includes the entire range of radio waves, infrared radiation, visible light, ultraviolet radiation, X-rays, and gamma rays.**

What Are Telescopes and How Do They Work?

Telescopes **are instruments that collect and focus light and other forms of electromagnetic radiation.** Telescopes make distant objects appear larger and brighter. A telescope that uses lenses or mirrors to collect and focus visible light is called an optical telescope. The two major types of optical telescopes are refracting telescopes and reflecting telescopes. Refracting telescopes use convex lenses to gather and focus light. A convex lens is a piece of glass that is curved, so the middle is thicker than the edges. A reflecting telescope uses a curved mirror to collect and focus light. The largest optical telescopes today are all reflecting telescopes because, while a mirror can be supported from below, a lens must be supported from the sides so that light can pass through it.

An observatory is a building that contains one or more telescopes. Because Earth's atmosphere makes objects in space look blurry, many large observatories are located on the tops of mountains or in space. Just as optical telescopes collect visible light, nonoptical telescopes collect and focus different types of electromagnetic radiation. Radio telescopes detect radio waves from objects in space. Other telescopes produce images in the infrared or X-ray portions of the spectrum.

6.1 Telescopes

Review and Reinforce

Understanding Main Ideas

Answer the following questions in your notebook.

1. What is electromagnetic radiation?

2. List the types of radiation in the electromagnetic spectrum.

3. Describe how telescopes work and explain why professional astronomers use large telescopes.

4. Explain the placement of optical telescopes.

Building Vocabulary

Match each term with its definition by writing the letter of the correct definition in the right column on the line beside the term in the left column.

5. _____ visible light

6. _____ telescope

7. _____ refracting telescope

8. _____ observatory

9. _____ convex lens

10. _____ wavelength

11. _____ radio telescope

12. _____ optical telescope

13. _____ reflecting telescope

a. building that houses telescopes

b. the crest-to-crest distance on a wave

c. instrument that collects and focuses electromagnetic radiation

d. an optical telescope that uses convex lenses to gather and focus light

e. an optical telescope that uses a curved mirror to gather and focus light

f. a telescope that collects radio waves

g. a piece of glass that is curved so the middle is thicker than the edges

h. electromagnetic radiation visible to the human eye

i. a telescope that collects and focuses visible light

Write About It

14. In your notebook, explain the difference between optical and nonoptical telescopes, and give examples of each.

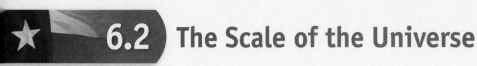

Key Concept Summaries

🔑 How Do Astronomers Measure Distances to the Stars?

Astronomers often use parallax to measure the distances to nearby stars. Parallax is the apparent change in position of an object when you look at it from different places. Astronomers note the position of a star, then they note its position six months later. They measure how much the star appears to move against a background of stars much farther away. The less the nearby star appears to move, the farther away it is. Parallax works as a measuring tool for distances up to a few hundred light-years from Earth.

🔑 How Do Astronomers Describe the Scale of the Universe?

Astronomers define the universe as all of space and everything in it. The universe is enormous. Astronomers study objects as close as the moon and as far away as quasars. They study huge objects, such as clusters of galaxies. They also study tiny particles, such as atoms within the stars.

Astronomers frequently use scientific notation to describe sizes and distances in the universe. They use a unit called the light-year to measure distances and sizes in the universe.

Scientific notation uses powers of ten to write very large or very small numbers in shorter form. Each number is written as the product of a number between 1 and 10 and a power of 10. For example, 1,200 is written as 1.2×10^3. Astronomers use a unit called a light-year to measure distances between stars. A light-year is the distance light travels in one year, about 9,460,000,000,000,000 meters (9.46×10^{15} meters in scientific notation). That's 9.46 trillion kilometers.

6.2 The Scale of the Universe

Review and Reinforce

Understanding Main Ideas

If the statement is true, write *true*. If the statement is false, change the underlined word or words to make the statement true.

1. _____ The spacecraft Voyager is 16,000,000,000 km away from Earth. That is the same as $\underline{1.6 \times 10^{10}}$ km.

2. _____ An astronomer says that his house cost 2.9×10^5. That is $\underline{\$2,900,000}$.

3. _____ A light-year is a measure of $\underline{time}$ on an astronomical scale.

4. _____ Astronomers often use $\underline{parallax}$ to measure distances to stars.

5. _____ $\underline{Refraction}$ makes nearby stars look like they shift position against the background of stars between winter and summer viewings from Earth.

6. _____ The $\underline{solar\ system}$ is all of space and everything in it.

Building Vocabulary

Write a definition for each of these terms on the lines below.

7. light-year

_____

_____

8. parallax

_____

_____

9. universe

_____

_____

10. scientific notation

_____

_____

6.3 Characteristics of Stars

Key Concept Summaries

🔑 How Are Stars Classified?

Stars are huge spheres of glowing gas. Made up mostly of hydrogen, stars produce energy through the process of nuclear fusion. **Characteristics used to classify stars include color, temperature, size, composition, and brightness.**

A star's color reveals its surface temperature. Blue stars are the hottest and red stars are coolest. Because they are so far away, all stars look about the same size, but they are not. Some, such as giant stars and supergiant stars, are much larger than our sun. Most stars are smaller than the sun. White dwarf stars are about the size of Earth, while tiny neutron stars are only about 20 kilometers in diameter.

The chemical composition of most stars is about 73 percent hydrogen, 25 percent helium, and 2 percent other elements by mass. But each star contains different amounts of various elements. Astronomers use a spectrograph to determine the elements found in a particular star. A spectrograph is a device that breaks light into colors and produces an image of the resulting spectrum. The gases in a star's atmosphere absorb some wavelengths of light produced within a star. On a spectrograph, each absorbed wavelength is shown as a dark line on the spectrum. Every chemical element has its own unique "fingerprint" of lines.

The brightness of a star depends upon both its size and temperature. A star's apparent brightness is the brightness as seen from Earth. Its absolute brightness is the brightness the star would have if it were at a standard distance from Earth.

🔑 What Is an H-R Diagram and How Do Astronomers Use It?

A Hertzsprung-Russell diagram is a graph of stars' surface temperature versus their absolute brightness. The points form a pattern. **Astronomers use H-R diagrams to classify stars and to understand how stars change over time.**

Most stars fall in a diagonal area of the diagram called the main sequence. The brightest stars are located near the top of an H-R diagram, while the dimmest stars are located at the bottom.

6.3 Characteristics of Stars

Review and Reinforce

Understanding Main Ideas

Fill in the blank to complete each statement.

Use the H-R diagram on the right to answer questions 1–5. Write your answers in the spaces provided.

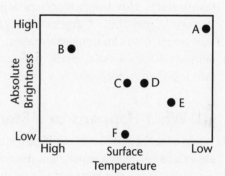

1. Star _____ has the greatest absolute brightness.

2. Star _____ has the greatest surface temperature.

3. Stars B, C, D, and E are probably _____
   _____ stars.

4. Star F is probably a(n) _____ star.

5. The three other characteristics used to classify stars are _____
   _____

Building Vocabulary

Write a definition for each of these terms in your notebook.

6. apparent brightness

7. spectrograph

8. Hertzsprung-Russell diagram

9. absolute brightness

10. main sequence

 Write About It

11. Look at the H-R diagram in your book, and locate the star Rigel. In your notebook, describe Rigel's color, surface temperature, absolute brightness, and what type of star it is.

Key Concept Summaries

🔑 How Does a Star Form and What Determines Its Life Span?

Stars do not last forever. Each star is born, goes through its life cycle, and eventually dies. **A star is born when the contracting gas and dust from a nebula becomes so dense and hot that nuclear fusion starts. How long a star lives depends on its mass.** A nebula is a large cloud of gas and dust spread out in an immense volume. In the densest part of a nebula, gravity pulls gas and dust together. A protostar is a contracting cloud of gas and dust with enough mass to form a star. A protostar is the earliest stage of a star's life. Nuclear fusion begins in a protostar.

Small-mass stars use up their fuel more slowly than large-mass stars, so they have much longer lives. While small-mass stars may live for as long as 200 billion years, a large mass star may live only about ten million years.

🔑 What Happens to a Star When It Runs Out of Fuel?

When a star begins to run out if fuel, it becomes either a red giant or a supergiant, depending on its mass. **After a star runs out of fuel, it becomes a white dwarf, a neutron star, or a black hole.**

As low-mass and medium-mass stars begin to run out of fuel, their outer layers expand and they become red giants. Eventually, their outer layers drift off into space, forming a glowing cloud of gas called a planetary nebula. The blue-white core of the star that is left behind cools and becomes a white dwarf. White dwarfs have about the mass of the sun but are only the size of Earth.

As high-mass stars begin to run out of fuel they become supergiants. When a supergiant runs out of fuel, it can explode suddenly. The explosion, a supernova, blazes millions of times brighter. The remains of the high-mass star may form a neutron star. A neutron star may be only 25 kilometers in diameter yet contain as much as three times the mass of the sun. Rapidly spinning neutron stars are called pulsars, which give off regular pulses of radio waves. If the original star was extremely massive, what remains after a supernova may be a black hole. A black hole is an object with gravity so strong that nothing, not even light, can escape.

6.4 Lives of Stars

Review and Reinforce

Understanding Main Ideas

Fill in each blank with the correct letter from the diagram.

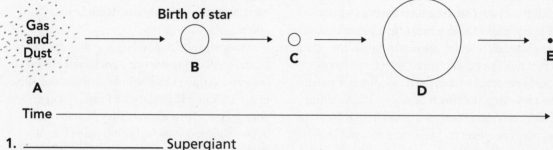

Gas and Dust

A

Birth of star

B

C

D

E

Time

1. _____ Supergiant

2. _____ Where fusion begins

3. _____ Part of a nebula

4. _____ White dwarf, neutron star, or black hole

5. _____ The stage the sun is in

Building Vocabulary

In your notebook, write a definition for each of these terms.

6. pulsar

7. white dwarf

8. nebula

9. protostar

10. supernova

11. neutron star

12. black hole

Write About It

13. In your notebook, compare and contrast red giants to supergiants. Include information about mass, how the star formed, and what the next stages in its life will be.

6.5 Star Systems and Galaxies

Key Concept Summaries

What Is a Star System?

Most stars are members of groups of two or more stars, called star systems. Star systems that have two stars are called double stars or binary stars. Often one star in a binary star is much brighter and more massive than the other. Even if only one star can be seen from Earth, astronomers can often detect its dimmer partner by observing the effects of its gravity. As a dim companion star revolves around a bright star, its gravity can cause the bright star to wobble. A dim star may also pass in front of a brighter star and eclipse it. A system in which one dim star blocks the light from another periodically is called an eclipsing binary. In 1995, astronomers first discovered a planet revolving around another star.

Again, they detected the planet by observing the effect the planet's gravity had on the star. Since then, astronomers have discovered more than 300 planets.

Many stars belong to larger groupings called clusters. All of the stars in a particular cluster formed from the same nebula at about the same time. An open cluster has a loose, disorganized appearance. Open clusters may contain up to a few thousand stars including many bright supergiants and a lot of gas and dust. Globular clusters are large groupings of older stars. They are round and can be packed with more than a million stars.

What Are the Major Types of Galaxies?

A galaxy is a huge group of single stars, star systems, star clusters, dust, and gas bound together by gravity. There are billions of galaxies in the universe. **Astronomers classify most galaxies into the following types: spiral, elliptical, and irregular.** From above, a spiral galaxy looks like a pinwheel. Elliptical galaxies look like round flattened balls. They contain billions of stars but have little gas or dust

between the stars. Stars are no longer forming inside them, so they contain only old stars. Irregular galaxies do not have regular shapes. They are smaller than spiral or elliptical galaxies. They contain young, bright stars and include a lot of gas and dust to form new ones. Quasars are active, young galaxies with black holes at their center. Gas spins around the black hole, heats up, and glows.

6.5 Star Systems and Galaxies

Review and Reinforce

Understanding Main Ideas

Answer the following questions in the spaces provided.

1. How can astronomers detect a binary star if only one of the two stars is visible from Earth?

   _____

   _____

2. What holds a galaxy together?

   _____

3. What type of galaxy is the Milky Way? _____

4. Which type of galaxy includes little gas and dust and no longer produces stars? _____

Building Vocabulary

Write a definition for each of these terms in your notebook.

5. binary star

6. eclipsing binary

7. open cluster

8. globular cluster

9. spiral galaxy

10. elliptical galaxy

11. irregular galaxy

12. quasar

Write About It

13. In your notebook, make a table that compares and contrasts the types of galaxies. Include galaxy shape, types of stars, amount of gas and dust, whether new stars form in them, and any special attributes in your table.

6.6 The Expanding Universe

Key Concept Summary

🔑 What Does the Big Bang Theory Say About the Universe?

Astronomers theorize that the universe began 13.8 billion years ago. At that time, the part of the universe we can see was no larger than the period at the end of this sentence. The universe then exploded in what astronomers call the big bang. **According to the big bang theory, the universe formed in an instant, billions of years ago, in an enormous explosion. New observations lead many astronomers to conclude that the universe will likely expand forever.**

Since the big bang, the universe has been expanding. In the 1920s, American astronomer Edwin Hubble discovered that almost all galaxies are moving away from us and from each other. Hubble's law states that the farther away a galaxy is, the faster it is moving away from us. Another piece of evidence for the big bang was the discovery of cosmic background radiation. Cosmic background radiation is the leftover thermal energy from the big bang. This energy was distributed in every direction as the universe expanded.

What will happen to the universe in the future? One possibility is that the universe will continue to expand. Another possibility is that the force of gravity will begin to pull the galaxies back together into a reverse big bang. The universe would be crushed in an enormous black hole. However, many astronomers believe the universe will likely expand forever.

Until recently, astronomers assumed that the universe consisted solely of the matter they could observe directly. But astronomer Vera Rubin discovered that the matter astronomers can see may make up as little as ten percent of the mass in the galaxies. The rest exists in the form of dark matter. Dark matter is matter that does not give off electromagnetic radiation. It cannot be seen directly. However, its presence can be inferred by observing the effect of its gravity on visible objects. In the late 1990s, astronomers observed that the expansion of the universe appeared to be accelerating. Astronomers infer that a mysterious new force, which they call dark energy, is causing the expansion of the universe to accelerate.

 **6.6** **The Expanding Universe**

Review and Reinforce

Understanding Main Ideas

Answer the following questions in the spaces provided.

1. What is Hubble's law?

_____

2. What did astronomer Edwin Hubble discover that led to the formulation of his law?

_____

_____

3. Give two pieces of evidence that support the big bang theory.

_____

_____

4. Why do scientists postulate that dark matter exists? Include an explanation of its name.

_____

_____

Building Vocabulary

Match each term with its definition by writing the letter of the correct definition in the right column on the line beside the term in the left column.

5. _____ big bang

6. _____ cosmic background radiation

7. _____ dark energy

8. _____ dark matter

a. a force that is causing the expansion of the universe to accelerate

b. leftover thermal energy from the formation of the universe

c. matter that does not give off electromagnetic radiation

d. the huge explosion that astronomers think was the birth of the universe

CHAPTER **6** Review

Read each question and choose the best answer.

---

1 The table below gives the characteristics of four different stars.

Star number	Relative size of star	Color of star
1	Small	White
2	Large	Blue
3	Giant	Red
4	Medium	Yellow

Using the information from the table, which of the stars is most likely the sun?

A Star 1

B Star 2

C Star 3

D Star 4

---

2 Which characteristic could a scientist observe with an optical telescope?

F Frequency of radio wave pulses from a neutron star

G Concentration of X-rays emitted near black holes

H Intensity of infrared rays emitted from the sun

J Shape of different-sized craters on the moon

3 The diagram shows the possible sequences of events in the life of a star.

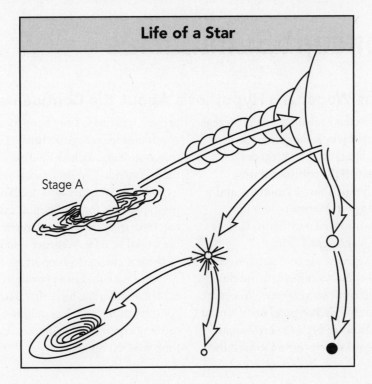

Life of a Star

Stage A

Which of the following best explains what happens at Stage A in the diagram?

A Gravity pulls together some of a nebula's dust and gas and forms a protostar in which nuclear fusion begins.

B Nuclear fusion takes place inside a nebula, and a protostar forms around the center of the fusion.

C A protostar absorbs energy from a nebula's dust and gas and increases in brightness.

D A protostar increases in mass as gas and dust from a nebula collect on it.

4 In 1965, two American physicists detected a faint amount of radiation coming from all directions of the night sky. This radiation was later called cosmic background radiation. Which observation of the cosmic background radiation supports the Big Bang Theory?

F It is thermal radiation.

G It was detected by a radio telescope.

H It is a very faint amount of radiation.

J It is distributed evenly throughout the night sky.

7.1 Continental Drift

Key Concept Summaries

🔑 What Was Wegener's Hypothesis About the Continents?

In 1910, a German scientist named Alfred Wegener became curious about why some continents look as though they could fit together. **Wegener's hypothesis was that all the continents were once joined together in a single landmass and have since drifted apart.** Wegener's idea that the continents slowly moved over Earth's surface became known as continental drift.

According to Wegener, the continents were joined together in a supercontinent, or single landmass, about 300 million years ago. Wegener called the supercontinent Pangaea. Over tens of millions of years, Pangaea began to break apart. The pieces of Pangaea slowly moved toward their present locations. They have come to form the continents we recognize today. Land features on the continents, such as mountain ranges and coal fields, provided Wegener with evidence for his hypothesis. Wegener also used fossils to support his hypothesis for continental drift. A fossil is any trace of an ancient organism that has been preserved in rock. Wegener also used evidence of climate change to support his hypothesis.

Wegener could not provide a satisfactory explanation for the force that pushes or pulls the continents. Because he could not identify the cause of continental drift, most geologists of his time rejected his idea.

🔑 What Is Sea-Floor Spreading?

In the 1950s, scientists mapped the ocean floor using sonar and discovered long mountain ranges. These mountain ranges, which scientists called mid-ocean ridges, had a valley along the top. In the 1960s, geologists observed that mid-ocean ridges continually add new material to the ocean floor in a process called sea-floor spreading. **Sea-floor spreading adds rock surface to the ocean floor, pushing older strips of rock outward from the ridge.**

🔑 What Occurs at Deep-Ocean Trenches?

The ocean floor is always spreading, but oceans do not take over Earth's surface. This is because the ocean floor plunges into the deep mantle in places, forming underwater canyons called deep-ocean trenches. **At deep-ocean trenches, old oceanic rock sinks slowly back into the mantle, in a process taking tens of millions of years.**

Subduction is the process by which ocean rock sinks beneath a deep-ocean trench and back into the mantle. As oceanic rock sinks into the hot mantle, swellings of magma rise through the crust.

7.1 Continental Drift

Review and Reinforce

Understanding Main Ideas

Answer the following questions in the spaces provided. Use a separate sheet of paper if you need more room.

1. State the hypothesis of continental drift.

   _____

   _____

2. Describe the land features that provided evidence for Wegener's hypothesis.

   _____

   _____

3. What role did the fossil *Glossopteris* play in Wegener's hypothesis?

   _____

   _____

4. How did Wegener use climate evidence to support his hypothesis?

   _____

   _____

5. Why did most scientists reject Wegener's theory for nearly half a century?

   _____

   _____

Building Vocabulary

Fill in the blank to complete each statement.

6. All the continents were joined together in a supercontinent that Wegener called _____.

7. _____ adds rock surface to the ocean floor.

8. The process by which ocean rock sinks beneath a deep-ocean trench and back into the deep mantle is called _____.

7.2 The Theory of Plate Tectonics

Key Concept Summary

🔑 What Is the Theory of Plate Tectonics?

The lithosphere is broken into separate sections, or plates, that carry pieces of continental and oceanic crust. Boundaries exist between these plates. Over time, these plates move and alter the location of continents and the shape of oceans. At a divergent boundary, plates move apart, or diverge, from each other. Mid-ocean ridges or rift valleys form at divergent boundaries. At a convergent boundary, plates converge, or come together. Mountains or volcanoes can form at convergent boundaries. Along a transform boundary, plates slide past each other. Earthquakes can occur at transform boundaries. Plate tectonics explains the formation, movement, and subduction of Earth's plates. **The theory of plate tectonics states that Earth's plates are in slow, constant motion, driven by convection currents in the mantle.**

The mantle is made of hot, solid rock. It lies beneath Earth's crust and consists of three regions. The upper mantle has rock like that in the crust. The mantle's middle region, or asthenosphere, is hotter and under more pressure than the upper region. The innermost region is more rigid than the asthenosphere and extends down to Earth's core.

Convection is the transfer of heat by the movement of a fluid (liquids and gases). The upward movement of warm fluid and the downward movement of cool fluid forms a flow called a convection current. Convection currents in Earth's mantle move Earth's plates.

7.2 The Theory of Plate Tectonics

Review and Reinforce

Understanding Main Ideas

Fill in the blank to complete each statement.

1. A deep-sea trench would be found at a _____ boundary at the bottom of the sea.

2. The North American _____ carries oceanic crust as well as the continental crust that contains North America.

3. Earthquakes occur near the San Andreas fault, which is located at a _____ boundary.

4. Where two continental plates collide with each other, _____ can form.

Building Vocabulary

Write a definition for each of these terms on the lines below.

5. transform boundary

_____

6. plate tectonics

_____

7. divergent boundary

_____

8. plates

_____

9. convergent boundary

_____

Write About It

10. In your notebook, describe what happens when dense oceanic crust collides with less-dense continental crust at a convergent boundary.

7.3) Forces in Earth's Crust

Key Concept Summaries

How Does Stress Change Earth's Crust?

As Earth's plates move, they can bend or fold rock. Forces created by movement of the Earth's plates are examples of stress. Stress adds energy to rock until the rock changes shape or breaks. Three kinds of stress can occur in the Earth's crust. **Tension, compression, and shearing work over millions of years to change the shape and volume of rock.**

Tension is the stress force that pulls on the crust and thins the rock in the middle. It happens where two plates pull apart. Compression is the stress force that squeezes rock until it folds or breaks. It happens where two plates come together and push against each other. Shearing is the stress force that pushes rock in two opposite directions. It happens where two plates slip past each other.

How Do Faults Form?

When enough stress builds up in rock, the rock breaks, creating a fault. The three main types of faults are normal faults, reverse faults, and strike-slip faults. Normal faults form where rock is pulled apart by tension in Earth's crust. The block above the angled fault is called the *hanging wall*. The rock below the fault is called the *footwall*. The hanging wall slips downward when rock moves along the fault.

A reverse fault has the same structure as a normal fault, but the hanging wall moves up and the footwall moves down. Reverse faults form where compression pushes the rock of the crust together. Shearing produces strike-slip faults. The rocks on either side of a strike-slip fault slip past each other and have little up or down motion. A strike-slip fault that forms the boundary between two plates is called a transform boundary.

How Does Plate Movement Create New Landforms?

Over millions of years, the forces of plate movement can change a flat plain into features such as anticlines and synclines, folded mountains, fault-block mountains, and plateaus. Folds are bends in rock that form when Earth's crust is compressed and gets shorter and thicker. A fold in rock that bends upward into an arch is an anticline. A fold that bends downward in a V shape is a syncline.

Tension forces create normal faults where two plates move away from each other. A fault-block mountain forms when the hanging walls of two normal faults drop down on either side of the footwall. Forces can also raise plateaus. A plateau is a large area of flat land that was lifted up high above sea level. Some plateaus form when forces in Earth's crust push up a large, flat block of rock.

7.3 Forces in Earth's Crust

Review and Reinforce

Understanding Main Ideas

Use the diagrams below to complete items 1–9.

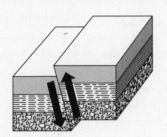 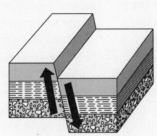 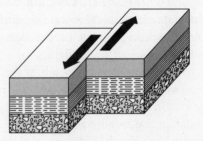

Diagram A   Diagram B   Diagram C

Diagram A

1. Type of Fault: _____

2. Stress Force: _____

3. Movement Along Fault: _____

Diagram B

4. Type of Fault: _____

5. Stress Force: _____

6. Movement Along Fault: _____

Diagram C

7. Type of Fault: _____

8. Stress Force: _____

9. Movement Along Fault: _____

Building Vocabulary

Write a definition for each of these terms in your notebook.

10. shearing

11. plateau

7.4 Volcanic Landforms

Key Concept Summaries

⚷ What Landforms Do Lava and Ash Create?

Volcanic eruptions create landforms made of lava, ash, and other materials. **Lava, ash, and other materials create shield volcanoes, cinder cone volcanoes, composite volcanoes, lava plateaus, and calderas.** Inside a caldera, a lake may form.

In an explosive eruption, ash, cinders, and clumps of lava called bombs can build up around the vent in a steep, cone-shaped hill or small mountain that is called a cinder cone. A cinder cone volcano may be hundreds of meters tall.

Composite volcanoes are tall, cone-shaped mountains in which layers of lava alternate with layers of ash. Composite volcanoes can be more than 4,800 meters tall. Thin layers of lava that pour out of a vent and harden on top of previous layers build a wide, gently sloping mountain called a shield volcano. Hot spot volcanoes on the ocean floor are usually shield volcanoes. Repeated floods of lava can form high, level plateaus called lava plateaus.

⚷ What Landforms Does Magma Create?

Sometimes magma cools and hardens into rock before reaching the surface. Over time, forces such as flowing water, ice, or wind may expose it. **Features formed by magma include volcanic necks, dikes, and sills, as well as dome mountains and batholiths.**

A volcanic neck forms when magma hardens in a volcano's pipe and the surrounding rock later

wears away. Magma that forces itself across rock layers hardens into a dike. Magma that squeezes between horizontal rock layers hardens to form a sill. A dome mountain forms when uplift pushes a large body of hardened magma toward the surface, which eventually becomes exposed. A batholith is a mass of rock formed when a large body of magma cools inside the crust.

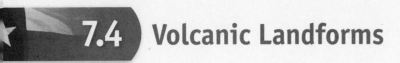

7.4 Volcanic Landforms

Review and Reinforce

Understanding Main Ideas

Answer the following questions in your notebook.

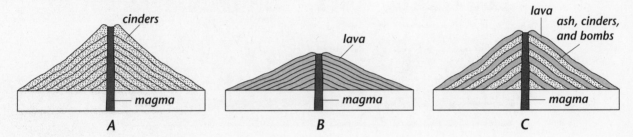

1. Name each type of volcano shown in the diagrams. How is each formed?

2. How does a lava plateau form?

3. What happens to create a caldera?

4. What are three features formed from magma?

5. How do landforms from magma form and become exposed?

Building Vocabulary

Write a definition for each of these terms in your notebook.

6. batholith

7. dike

8. volcanic neck

9. sill

10. caldera

 ## Write About It

11. In your notebook, summarize the landforms formed from lava and magma.

CHAPTER **7** **Review**

Read each question and choose the best answer.

_____

1 When two plates in Earth's crust move apart from one another, normal faults are created as shown in the diagram.

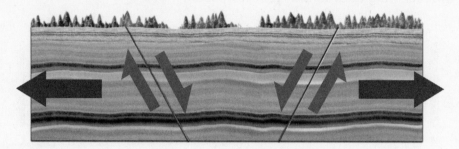

Which of the following landforms could result from this movement?

A Fault-block mountain

B Folded mountain

C Plateau

D Valley

_____

2 Which of the following best explains why scientists initially rejected Alfred Wegener's theory of continental drift?

F There was no evidence indicating that the continents would fit together in the arrangement that Wegener proposed.

G There was no evidence from land features to suggest that the continents were once connected in one mass.

H There was no evidence to explain how the continents could have moved apart from one another.

J There was no fossil evidence to suggest that the continents were once connected in one mass.

3 What type of plate boundary is represented in the diagram below?

  A Divergent boundary

  B Convergent boundary

  C Transform boundary

  D None of the above

4 El Chinchon is a volcano in Mexico. It is located near a subduction zone of two tectonic plates. After its explosive eruption in 1982, a large caldera formed. The volcano has not erupted since.

Which of the following might a person see when visiting the eruption site today?

  F A lake

  G A lava plateau

  H A transform fault

  J A composite volcano

8.1 The Earth System

Key Concept Summaries

🔑 What Are the Main Parts of the Earth System?

A system is a group of parts that work together as a whole. The Earth system involves a constant flow of matter though different parts. The constant flow, or cycling, of matter through the Earth system is driven by energy. Energy is the ability to do work. The energy that drives the Earth system has two main sources: heat from the sun and heat flowing out of Earth as it cools.

The Earth system has four main spheres: the atmosphere, the hydrosphere, the geosphere, and the biosphere. As a major source of energy for Earth processes, the sun can be considered part of the Earth system as well.

Earth's atmosphere is the relatively thin envelope of gases that form Earth's outermost layer. Earth's geosphere has three main parts: a metal core, a solid middle layer, and a rocky outer layer. The hydrosphere contains all of Earth's water. The part of Earth that contains living organisms makes up the biosphere.

When feedback occurs, a system returns—or feeds back—to itself data about a change in the system. Feedback demonstrates how changes in one part of the Earth system might affect the other parts.

🔑 How Do Forces Change Earth?

Lands are constantly being created and destroyed by competing forces. Forces that construct, or build up, mountains are called constructive forces. **Constructive forces shape the land's surface by building up mountains and other landmasses.** Volcanoes build up Earth's surface by spewing lava that hardens into rock. Earthquakes build landmasses by lifting up mountains and rock.

Forces such as ice, rain, wind, and changing temperatures break down rock in a process called weathering. These are called destructive forces. **Destructive forces destroy and wear away landmasses through the process of weathering.** Erosion is the carrying away of land by natural forces such as water, ice, wind, or gravity.

🔑 What Features Do Constructive and Destructive Forces Form?

Eroded materials are eventually deposited in new locations. The process by which sediment is laid down in new locations is called deposition. Weathering, erosion, and deposition create depositional and erosional features. **Depositional**

features include deltas and meanders. Erosional features include valleys and canyons. Like land features, erosional features are reshaped by weathering.

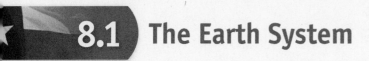

8.1 The Earth System

Review and Reinforce

Understanding Main Ideas

Answer the following questions in the spaces provided. Use a separate sheet of paper if you need more room.

1. What are the four main spheres of the Earth system?

   _____

2. Explain why constructive forces and destructive forces are considered to be competing forces.

   _____

3. How do constructive forces change the land's surface?

   _____

4. How do destructive forces change the land's surface?

   _____

Building Vocabulary

Match each term with its definition by writing the letter of the correct definition in the right column on the line beside the term in the left column.

5. _____ biosphere

6. _____ energy

7. _____ hydrosphere

8. _____ destructive forces

9. _____ constructive forces

10. _____ atmosphere

11. _____ geosphere

12. _____ deposition

a. the ability to do work

b. forces that construct, or build up, mountains

c. the thin envelope of gases forming Earth's outermost layer

d. the sphere that contains all of Earth's water

e. the part of Earth that contains living organisms

f. Earth's metal core, solid middle layer, and outer rocky layer

g. the process by which sediment is laid down in new locations

h. forces that wear down, or destroy, landmasses

 **8.2** Exploring Earth's Surface

Key Concept Summaries

🔑 What Does the Topography of an Area Include?

Topography is the shape of the land. An area's topography may be flat, sloping, hilly, or mountainous. **The topography of an area includes the area's elevation, relief, and landforms.**

The height above sea level of a point on Earth's surface is its elevation. The difference in elevation between the highest and lowest parts of an area is its relief. The Rocky Mountains include huge mountains separated by deep valleys. These areas have high relief, or great differences in elevation.

There are many different landforms. A landform is a feature of topography, such as a hill or valley, formed by the processes that shape Earth's surface. Different landforms have different combinations of elevation and relief.

🔑 What Are the Main Types of Landforms?

Landforms vary greatly in size and shape. **Three major types of landforms are plains, mountains, and plateaus.** A plain is a landform made up of nearly flat or gently rolling land with low relief. A plain that lies along a seacoast is called a coastal plain. A plain that lies away from the coast is called an interior plain. The broad interior plains of North America are called the Great Plains. A mountain is a landform with high elevation and high relief. A mountain's base can cover an area of several square kilometers or more. A mountain range is a group of mountains that are closely related in shape, structure, area, and age. A landform that has high elevation and a more or less level surface is called a plateau. The Columbia Plateau in Washington State is an example.

A large area of land where the topography is made up mainly of one type of landform is called a landform region. The Great Plains and Rocky Mountains are examples of major landform regions. Other terms used to describe landform regions include uplands, which are regions of hilly topography, and lowlands, which are regions of plains with low elevations.

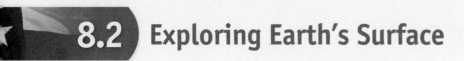

8.2 Exploring Earth's Surface

Review and Reinforce

Understanding Main Ideas

Fill in the table below.

Landform	Elevation	Relief
Plains	Low or high	1.
2.	High	High
3.	High	Low

Answer the following questions in your notebook.

4. Explain why mountains, hills, and valleys are landforms.

5. Compare and contrast a mountain range with a mountain system.

Building Vocabulary

Match each term with its definition by writing the letter of the correct definition in the right column on the line beside the term in the left column.

6. _____ plateau

7. _____ topography

8. _____ elevation

9. _____ relief

10. _____ landform region

11. _____ plain

a. the height above sea level of a point on Earth's surface

b. the shape of the land

c. flat or gently rolling land with low relief

d. a large area of land for which the topography is mainly one type of landform

e. the difference in elevation between the highest and the lowest parts of an area

f. a landform that has high elevation and a more or less level surface

Write About It

12. In you notebook, describe the topography of the landform region called the Atlantic Coastal Plain.

8.3 Models of Earth

Key Concept Summaries

🔑 How Do Maps and Globes Represent Earth?

A globe is a sphere that represents Earth's entire surface. A map is a flat model of all or part of Earth's surface as seen from above. **Maps and globes are drawn to scale and use symbols to represent features on Earth's surface. To show Earth's curved surface on a flat map, mapmakers use map projections.** A map projection is a framework of lines that helps to transfer points on Earth's three-dimensional surface onto a flat map. Mapmakers use shapes and pictures called symbols to stand for features on Earth's surface. A map's key, or legend, is a list of all the symbols used on the map. A map's scale relates distance on a map to that on Earth's surface.

🔑 How Is Distance Measured in Degrees?

Distances on Earth are measured in degrees from the equator and the prime meridian. A degree (°) is $\frac{1}{360}$ of the distance around a circle.

Halfway between the North and South poles, the equator forms an imaginary line that circles Earth. The equator divides Earth into the Northern and Southern hemispheres. A hemisphere is one half of the sphere that makes up Earth's surface. Another imaginary line, the prime meridian, makes a half circle from the North Pole to the South Pole.

🔑 What Are Latitude and Longitude?

Using the equator and the prime meridian, mapmakers have constructed a grid made up of lines of latitude and longitude. **The lines of latitude and longitude form a grid that can be used to find locations anywhere on Earth.**

The equator is the starting line for measuring latitude, or distance in degrees north or south of the equator. Between the equator and each pole are 90 evenly spaced, parallel lines of latitude. The distance in degrees east or west of the prime meridian is called longitude. There are 360 lines of longitude that run from north to south, meeting at the poles. The location of any point on Earth's surface can be expressed in terms of latitude and longitude lines that cross at that point.

8.3 Models of Earth

Review and Reinforce

Understanding Main Ideas

Fill in the blanks on the diagram below.

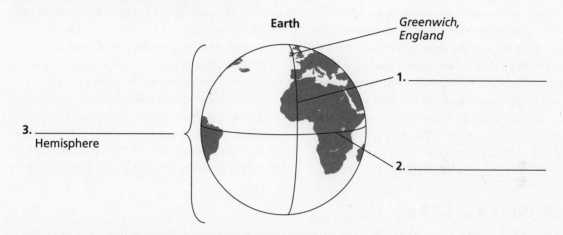

Earth

Greenwich, England

1. _____

2. _____

3. _____
   Hemisphere

Answer the following questions in your notebook.

4. What's the difference between a map and a map projection?

5. Washington, D.C., is found at 39° N 77° W. Explain what this statement means.

Building Vocabulary

Match each term with its definition by writing the letter of the correct definition in the right column on the line beside the term in the left column.

6. ____ globe

7. ____ longitude

8. ____ latitude

9. ____ hemisphere

10. ____ key

11. ____ prime meridian

12. ____ equator

a. a list of all the symbols used on a map with an explanation of their meaning

b. the imaginary line from the North Pole to the South Pole that passes through Greenwich, England

c. the distance in degrees north and south of the equator

d. one half of the sphere that makes up Earth's surface

e. a sphere that represents Earth's entire surface

f. the distance in degrees east or west of the prime meridian

g. the imaginary line that circles Earth halfway between the north and south poles

 **8.4** Mapping Technology

Key Concept Summaries

How Are Maps Made?

In surveying, mapmakers determine distances and elevations using instruments and the principles of geometry. **Today, computers produce maps using data from many sources, including satellites and aerial photographs. Computers allow mapmakers to store, process, and display map data electronically.**

All the data used in computer mapping must be written in numbers. The process by which mapmakers convert the location of map points to numbers is called digitizing. Each bit of a digital image is called a pixel. Often appearing as a small square or dot, each pixel represents a tiny piece of the image.

Aerial photographs also provide map data. Aerial photographs are usually taken by cameras mounted in airplanes. As the plane fires, the cameras take pictures of strips of land. Computer mapping also makes use of satellite data. Mapping satellites use electronic devices to collect computer data about the land surface. Pictures of the surface based on these data are called satellite images.

What Are GPS and GIS?

Advancing computer technology has brought new tools to mapmakers. **GPS (Global Positioning System) uses satellite data to help users locate their positions anywhere on or above Earth. GIS (Geographic Information System) uses GPS and other electronic sources to display and analyze geographic data.**

The Global Positioning System, or GPS, is a navigational system that uses satellite signals to fix the location of a radio receiver on Earth's surface. A Geographic Information System, or GIS, is a system of computer hardware and software used to produce interactive maps of many kinds. The different types of information stored in a GIS are called *data layers*. GIS users can combine the information from the data layers to solve problems and answer questions.

8.4 Mapping Technology

Review and Reinforce

Understanding Main Ideas
Fill in the blanks in the flowchart below.

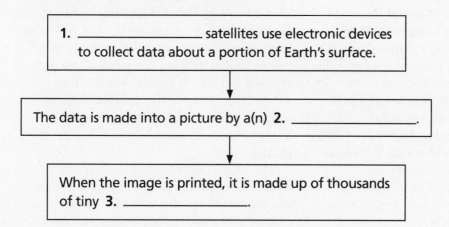

1. _____ satellites use electronic devices to collect data about a portion of Earth's surface.

The data is made into a picture by a(n) **2.** _____.

When the image is printed, it is made up of thousands of tiny **3.** _____.

Answer the following questions in your notebook.

4. What sources do computers use to make maps?

5. What kinds of features are shown by satellite images?

6. What is a GIS and for what is it used?

Building Vocabulary
Fill in the blank to complete each statement.

7. The process by which mapmakers convert the location of map points to numbers is called _____.

8. Pictures of Earth's surface based on data collected by satellites are called _____.

9. Each bit that makes up a satellite image is called a(n) _____.

10. The _____ is a system for navigation that uses satellite signals to find the location of a radio receiver on Earth's surface.

 **8.5** Interpreting Topographic Maps

Key Concept Summary

🔑 How Do Topographic Maps Show Earth's Features?

A topographic map is a map showing the surface features of an area. **Topographic maps show Earth's features by using contour lines and a contour interval.** On a topographic map, a contour line connects points of equal elevation.

The change in elevation from one contour line to the next is called the contour interval. The contour interval for a given map is always the same. Every fifth contour line, known as an index contour, is darker and heavier than the others.

To read a topographic map, you must familiarize yourself with the map's scale and interpret the map's contour lines. In the United States, many topographic maps are drawn at a scale of 1 : 24,000, or 1 centimeter equals 0.24 kilometers.

To find the elevation of a feature, begin at the labeled index contour. Then, count the number of contour lines up or down to the feature. Closely spaced contour lines indicate steep slopes. Widely spaced contour lines indicate gentle slopes or a relatively flat area. A contour line that forms a closed loop with no other contour lines inside indicates a hilltop. A closed loop with dashes inside indicates a depression, or hollow in the ground.

The shape of contour lines also helps to show ridges and valleys. V-shaped contour lines pointing downhill indicate a ridge line. V-shaped contour lines pointing uphill indicate a valley. A stream in the valley flows toward the open end of the V.

 **8.5** Interpreting Topographic Maps

Review and Reinforce

Understanding Main Ideas

Answer the following questions in your notebook.

1. What three things do mapmakers use topographic maps to represent?

2. How can index contours be identified?

3. You see that a topographic map of your area has a scale of 1 : 24,000. What does this tell you?

4. Can a contour line on a topographic map connect a point with an elevation of 100 feet to a point with an elevation of 110 feet? Explain why or why not.

5. On a topographic map, how would you show an island in the ocean with an elevation of 80 feet if the contour interval is 10 feet?

6. How could a person who snow skis or hikes use a topographic map?

Building Vocabulary

Fill in the blank to complete each statement.

7. The change in elevation from one contour line to the next is called the _____.

8. _____ are lines on a map labeled with the elevation.

9. A(n) _____ connects points of equal elevation on a topographic map.

10. A(n) _____ map shows the surface features of an area.

 Write About It

11. In your notebook, explain why topographic maps make good maps for hikers.

8.6 Interpreting Satellite Views

Key Concept Summary

🔑 How Do Satellite Views Show Earth's Features?

Satellite views show Earth's land features with a combination of color and shading. Shading can show the contours of steep mountains. A lack of shading can indicate flat plains. Shading can also provide information about land elevation. Color can show areas of land and water. Land areas with vegetation are green. Land areas that are bare or rocky are brown. Areas of water are blue.

You can identify erosional features in satellite views by analyzing the color and shading in the image. Shape helps you identify depositional features. These features include valleys, canyons, and deltas. Canyons and other depressions in the land have a dark shading pattern. These patterns give you information about the contours of these features.

8.6 Interpreting Satellite Views

Review and Reinforce

Understanding Main Ideas
Fill in the blank to complete each statement.

1. Satellite views show Earth's land _____, such as water, rock, or vegetation.

2. A narrow black line at the base of a canyon is likely to be a _____.

3. A forested area in summer in a satellite view would have a _____ color.

4. Shading can provide information about the height of a mountain, or its _____.

5. A wide area on a satellite photo that has no shading is likely to be a flat _____.

6. Colors and _____ can help you to identify erosional features in a satellite view.

Building Vocabulary
Write a definition for the term on the lines below.

7. erosional feature

_____

_____

Write About It

8. In your notebook, describe what an area of high, rocky mountains would look like in a satellite view.

Name _____ Date _____ Class _____

Read each question and choose the best answer.

---

1 You are looking at a topographic map of a nearby state park. The contour interval is 150 feet, and the scale is 1:24,000. In one area of the map, there are three contour lines in 4.2 cm.

Which of the following accurately describes the land represented by this portion of the map?

A The hill rises 450 feet in 100,800 feet.

B The hill rises 630 feet in 24,000 feet.

C The hill rises 450 feet in 1 kilometer.

D The hill rises 630 feet in 0.24 kilometers.

---

2 A certain river is shown on a topographic map. The contour lines that cross the river form a "V" shape that points uphill. How will the contour lines on the map need to change after the river has weathered the mountain for several centuries?

F The contour lines will form a sharper "V" shape pointing uphill.

G The contour lines will form a wide "U" shape pointing uphill.

H The contour lines will form a sharper "V" shape pointing downhill.

J The contour lines will form a wide "U" shape pointing downhill.

3 A topographic map of a small coastal town is shown.

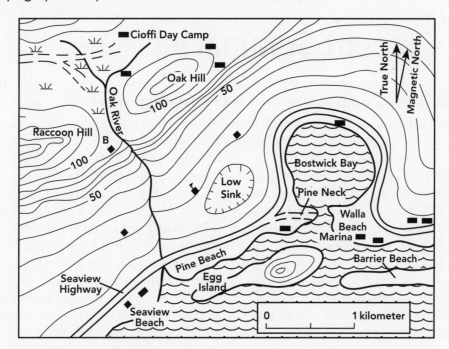

How do Raccoon Hill and Oak Hill compare to one another?

A Oak Hill is taller than Raccoon Hill.

B Oak Hill is steeper than Raccoon Hill.

C Oak Hill covers more area than Raccoon Hill.

D Oak Hill is farther from the ocean than Raccoon Hill.

4 Scientists have analyzed satellite images of Mars and found features such as channels and ancient floodplains. Scientists also found evidence of alluvial fans, fan-shaped deposits of sediment, in the satellite images. Which of the following hypotheses about the surface of Mars is supported by this evidence?

F It used to have running water.

G It used to experience strong winds.

H It has been shaped by plate tectonics.

J It used to be occupied by living organisms.

9.1 The Air Around You

Key Concept Summaries

🗝 What is the Composition of Earth's Atmosphere?

Weather is the condition of Earth's atmosphere at a particular time and place. Earth's **atmosphere** is the envelope of gases that surrounds the planet. **Earth's atmosphere consists of nitrogen, oxygen, carbon dioxide, water vapor, and other gases, as well as particles of liquids and solids.**

The most abundant gas in the atmosphere is nitrogen. It makes up a little more than three fourths of the air we breathe. Oxygen, the second most abundant gas, makes up about 21 percent of the volume. Plants and animals take oxygen from air and use it to release the energy in food. Oxygen is also necessary for fire to burn. Carbon dioxide makes up much less than 1 percent of the atmosphere, but it is essential to life. Plants must have carbon dioxide to produce food. Together,

oxygen and nitrogen make up 99 percent of dry air. The other one percent is mostly argon, plus other gases in amounts so small that they are described as trace gases.

So far, we've discussed the composition of dry air. But in reality, air is not dry. Air contains **water vapor,** or water in the form of a gas. Water vapor is invisible. It is not the same thing as steam, which is made up of tiny droplets of liquid water. Clouds form when water vapor condenses out of the air to form tiny droplets of liquid water or crystals of ice. If these droplets or crystals become heavy enough, they fall as rain or snow. Air also contains tiny solid and liquid particles of dust, smoke, salt, and chemicals.

🗝 How Is the Atmosphere a System?

The atmosphere is a system that interacts with other Earth systems, such as the ocean. The atmosphere has many different parts, such as clouds, air, wind, and energy. **Events in one part of the atmosphere affect other parts of the atmosphere.**

Energy from the sun drives the motions in the atmosphere. For example, a storm such as a hurricane involves a great deal of energy. A hurricane gets energy from warm ocean water, which gets its heat from the sun.

9.1 The Air Around You

Review and Reinforce

Understanding Main Ideas

If the statement is true, write *true***. If the statement is false, change the underlined word or words to make the statement true.**

1. _____, _____ More than three fourths of the air we breathe is <u>oxygen</u>.

2. _____ <u>Argon</u> is the second most abundant gas in air.

3. _____ Plants need <u>carbon dioxide</u> to produce food.

4. _____ Without <u>nitrogen</u> in the air, a fire will not burn.

5. _____ When fuels such as coal and gasoline are burned they release <u>nitrogen</u> into the air.

6. _____ Condensed water vapor in the atmosphere forms <u>clouds</u>.

7. _____ Energy from the <u>wind</u> drives the motions in the atmosphere.

Building Vocabulary

In your notebook, write a definition for each of these terms.

8. atmosphere

9. water vapor

10. weather

 ### Write About It

11. In your notebook, describe the composition of Earth's atmosphere and give an example of how events in one part affect other parts of the atmosphere.

9.2 Air Pressure

Key Concept Summaries

🗝 What Are Some Properties of Air?

Air is made up of atoms and molecules, which have mass. **Because air has mass, it also has other properties, including density and pressure.** The amount of mass in a given volume of air is its density. You calculate the density of a substance by dividing its mass by its volume.

The force pushing on an area or surface is called pressure. Air pressure is the result of the weight of a column of air pushing on an area. The reason air pressure does not crush you is because the molecules in air push in all directions. So the air pushing down is balanced by the air pushing up.

🗝 What Instruments Measure Air Pressure?

Air pressure can change daily. A barometer is an instrument that is used to measure air pressure. **The two common kinds of barometers are mercury barometers and aneroid barometers.**

A mercury barometer consists of a long glass tube that is closed at one end and open at the other. The open end rests in a dish of mercury. The closed end contains very little air. Increases in air pressure force the column of mercury higher in the tube. The level of the

mercury in the tube shows the pressure of the air that day. An aneroid barometer has an airtight metal chamber. When air pressure increases, the thin walls of the chamber are pushed in. When air pressure drops, the walls bulge out. As the chamber's shape changes a needle on the dial moves. Weather reports air pressure in inches of mercury. National Weather service maps indicate air pressure in millibars. One inch of mercury equals about 33.86 millibars.

🗝 How Does Altitude Affect Air Pressure and Density?

Altitude, or elevation, is distance above sea level. **Air pressure decreases as altitude increases. As air pressure decreases, so does density.** Because air is less dense at a high altitude, each

cubic meter of air you breathe has fewer oxygen molecules than at sea level. So you would become short of breath more quickly at a high altitude.

9.2 Air Pressure

Review and Reinforce

Understanding Main Ideas

Fill in the blank to complete each statement. Use the illustration to answer Questions 3–5.

1. When air pressure increases, the liquid in a mercury barometer _____.

2. An aneroid barometer does not use _____.

3. Air pressure is greater at point _____.

4. Altitude is greater at point _____.

5. Density of the air is greater at point _____.

Building Vocabulary

In your notebook, write a definition for each of these terms.

6. air pressure

7. barometer

8. density

9. mercury barometer

10. aneroid barometer

11. altitude

 Write About It

12. In your notebook, explain what air density and air pressure are and how altitude affects these properties of air.

9.3 Layers of the Atmosphere

Key Concept Summaries

🔑 What Are the Four Main Layers of the Atmosphere?

Scientists divide Earth's atmosphere into four main layers classified according to changes in temperature. These layers are the troposphere, the stratosphere, the mesosphere, and the thermosphere.

🔑 What Are the Characteristics of the Atmosphere's Layers?

The troposphere is the lowest layer of Earth's atmosphere. *Tropo-* means "turning" or "changing." Conditions in the troposphere are more variable than in the other layers. **The troposphere is the layer of the atmosphere in which Earth's weather occurs.** At about 12 kilometers thick, it is the thinnest and most dense layer. It contains almost all the mass of the atmosphere. On average, for every 1-kilometer increase in altitude, the air gets about 6.5°C cooler.

The stratosphere extends from the top of the troposphere to about 50 kilometers above Earth's surface. *Strato-* means "layer" or "spread out." **The stratosphere is the second layer of the atmosphere and contains the ozone layer.** The lower stratosphere is cold, about –60°C. The upper stratosphere is warmer because the ozone layer absorbs energy from the sun.

Above the stratosphere a drop in temperature marks the beginning of the next layer, the mesosphere. *Meso-* means "middle." The mesosphere extends from about 50 kilometers to 80 kilometers above Earth's surface. In the upper mesosphere, temperatures approach –90°C. **The mesosphere is the layer of the atmosphere that protects Earth's surface from being hit by most meteoroids.**

The outermost layer of Earth's atmosphere is the thermosphere. The thermosphere extends from 80 kilometers above Earth's surface outward into space. It has no definite outer limit. Gas molecules in the thermosphere move fast, so the temperature is very high. But the molecules are spaced far apart. The thermosphere has two layers. The lower layer, the ionosphere, extends from about 80 kilometers to 400 kilometers above Earth's surface. The outer layer, the exosphere, extends from about 400 kilometers outward for thousands of kilometers.

9.3 Layers of the Atmosphere

Review and Reinforce

Understanding Main Ideas
Fill in the blank to complete each statement.

1. The middle layer of Earth's atmosphere is the _____.

2. The upper region of the stratosphere is warm because energy from the sun is absorbed by the _____.

3. The exosphere is the outer layer of the _____.

4. The _____ contains almost all the mass of the atmosphere.

5. The _____ is thicker over the equator than over the poles.

6. The lower layer of the thermosphere is the _____.

Building Vocabulary
In your notebook, write a definition for each of these terms.

7. stratosphere

8. thermosphere

9. troposphere

10. mesosphere

 ### Write About It
11. In your notebook, describe the characteristics of the four main layers of the atmosphere.

9.4 Energy in Earth's Atmosphere

Key Concept Summaries

🔑 How Does Energy From the Sun Travel to Earth?

Nearly all the energy in Earth's atmosphere comes from the sun. This energy travels to Earth as **electromagnetic waves,** a form of energy that can move through the vacuum of space. Electromagnetic waves can be classified according to wavelength, or distance between wave peaks. **Most of the energy from the sun travels to Earth in the form of visible light and infrared radiation. A smaller amount arrives as ultraviolet radiation.**

Visible light includes all the colors of the rainbow. The different colors you see are the result of different wavelengths. The direct transfer of energy by electromagnetic waves is called **radiation.** One form, **infrared radiation,** has wavelengths longer than red light. It is invisible to humans but can be felts as heat. The sun also gives off **ultraviolet radiation,** which is an invisible form of energy with wavelengths shorter than violet light.

🔑 What Happens to the Sun's Energy When It Reaches Earth?

Some sunlight is absorbed or reflected by the atmosphere before it can reach the surface. The rest passes through the atmosphere to the surface. Different wavelengths of radiation are absorbed by different layers in the atmosphere. Some ultraviolet radiation is absorbed by the ozone layer. Infrared radiation passes farther before some is absorbed by water vapor and carbon dioxide. In the troposphere, clouds reflect some sunlight back into space. Dust-sized particles and gases in the atmosphere disperse light in all directions in a process called **scattering.**

About 50 percent of the sun's energy that reaches Earth's surface is absorbed. It heats land and water. **Earth's surface radiates some energy back into the atmosphere as infrared radiation.** Some travels all the way back into space, but much is absorbed by water vapor, carbon dioxide and other gases in the air. These gases hold heat in the atmosphere in a process called the **greenhouse effect.** The greenhouse effect keeps Earth's atmosphere at a comfortable temperature. But scientists have evidence that human activities may be altering this process.

9.4 Energy in Earth's Atmosphere

Review and Reinforce

Understanding Main Ideas

If the statement is true, write *true*. **If the statement is false, change the underlined word or words to make the statement true.**

1. _____ Electromagnetic waves are classified according to <u>wavelength</u>.

2. _____ Visible light with the <u>shortest</u> wavelengths are red and orange light.

3. _____ Infrared radiation is <u>visible</u> to humans.

4. _____ During the day, the sky appears blue because of <u>scattering</u>.

5. _____ As it passes through the atmosphere, some <u>infrared</u> radiation is absorbed by the ozone layer.

Building Vocabulary

Match each term with its definition by writing the letter of the correct definition in the right column on the line beside the term in the left column.

6. _____ electromagnetic waves

7. _____ radiation

8. _____ infrared radiation

9. _____ ultraviolet radiation

10. _____ scattering

11. _____ greenhouse effect

a. a form of energy with wavelengths that are longer than those of red light

b. the direct transfer of energy by electromagnetic waves

c. reflection of light in all directions

d. a form of energy that can travel through space

e. the process by which gases in the atmosphere hold heat

f. a form of energy with wavelengths that are shorter than those of violet light

Write About It

12. In your notebook, briefly explain how energy from the sun travels to Earth and describe what happens to this energy as it passes through the atmosphere.

9.5 Heat Transfer

Key Concept Summaries

🌡 How Is Temperature Measured?

All substances are made up of tiny particles (atoms and molecules) that are constantly moving. The faster the particles move, the more energy they have. Thermal energy measures the *total* energy of motion in the particles of a substance. Temperature is the *average* amount of energy of motion of each particle of a substance. **Air temperature is usually measured with a thermometer.** A thermometer is a device that measures temperature. Temperature is measured in units called degrees. Two temperature scales are the Celsius scale and the Fahrenheit scale.

🌡 How Is Heat Transferred?

Heat is thermal energy that is transferred from a hotter object to a cooler one. **Heat is transferred in three ways: convection, conduction, and radiation.** Atoms and molecules in fluids (liquids and gases) can move easily. As they move, their energy moves with them. The transfer of heat by the movement of a fluid is called convection. The transfer of heat between two substances that are in direct contact is called conduction. When a fast moving molecule bumps into a slower moving molecule, the faster one transfers some of its energy to the slower one. The closer together the molecules are in a substance, the better they conduct heat. Conduction works best in some solids, such as metals, but not as well in liquids and gases. Radiation is the direct transfer of energy by electromagnetic waves. Most of the heat that you feel from the sun travels to you as infrared radiation, which you cannot see but can feel.

Radiation, conduction, and convection work together to heat the troposphere. During a sunny day the land gets warmer than the air. But because air doesn't conduct heat well, only the first few meters of the troposphere are heated by conduction. When air at ground level warms, its molecules spread out, making it less dense. Cooler denser air sinks toward the surface, forcing the warmer air to rise. The upward movement of warm air and the downward movement of cool air form convection currents. **Heat is transferred mostly by convection within the troposphere.**

9.5 Heat Transfer

Review and Reinforce

Understanding Main Ideas

If the statement is true, write *true*. If the statement is false, change the underlined word or words to make the statement true.

1. _____ In the troposphere, heat is transferred mostly by <u>conduction</u>.

2. _____ Conduction works best in some <u>solids</u>.

3. _____ Air temperature is usually measured with a <u>barometer</u>.

4. _____ The upward movement of warm air and the downward movement of cool air form a <u>convection current</u>.

5. _____ The <u>farther apart</u> the molecules in a substance are, the better they conduct heat.

6. _____ In the <u>Fahrenheit</u> temperature scale, water freezes at 0° and boils at 100°.

Building Vocabulary

In your notebook, write a definition for each of these terms.

7. heat

8. conduction

9. thermal energy

10. convection

Write About It

11. In your notebook, explain how energy from the sun becomes thermal energy on Earth and how that energy raises the temperature of the troposphere.

9.6 Winds

Key Concept Summaries

🔑 What Causes Winds?

Differences in air pressure cause the air to move. Wind is the movement of air parallel to Earth's surface. Winds move from areas of high pressure to areas of lower pressure. **Most differences in air pressure are caused by the unequal heating of the atmosphere by the sun.** As air over heated surfaces expands and becomes less dense, its air pressure decreases.

If nearby air is cooler, it will flow under the warmer, less dense air. Winds are described by their direction, determined with a wind vane, and speed, measured with an anemometer. A wind is named for the direction it blows from. The increased cooling that a wind can cause is called the windchill factor.

🔑 How Do Local Winds and Global Winds Differ?

Winds that blow over short distances are called local winds. **The unequal heating of Earth's surface within a small area causes local winds.** Local winds form only when large-scale winds are weak. Two types of local winds are sea breezes and land breezes. A sea breeze or lake breeze is a local wind that blows from an ocean or lake. During the day land warms faster than water. The air above the land heats and rises, and cool air from the ocean flows in to take its place. At night the process is reversed, land cools faster than the ocean. The flow of air from land to a body of water forms a land breeze.

Global winds are winds that blow steadily from specific directions over long distances. **Like local winds, global winds are created by the unequal heating of Earth's surface. But unlike local winds, global winds occur over a large area.** Because of Earth's spherical shape, rays from the sun strike directly at the equator but hit

the poles at an angle. As a result, temperatures near the poles are much lower than near the equator. The difference produces giant convection currents in the atmosphere. Surface winds blow from the poles toward the equator. Higher in the atmosphere, winds flow from equator to poles. The way Earth's rotations make winds curve is called the Coriolis effect. Because of the Coriolis effect, global winds in the Northern Hemisphere gradually turn toward the right. A wind blowing toward the south gradually turns toward the southwest. In the Southern Hemisphere, winds curve toward the left. The Coriolis effect and other factors combine to produce a pattern of wind belts and calm areas around Earth. These include doldrums, horse latitudes, trade winds, prevailing westerlies, and polar easterlies. Latitude is the distance from the equator, measured in degrees.

9.6 Winds

Review and Reinforce

Understanding Main Ideas
Answer the following questions in the spaces provided.

1. How does heating air affect its density and pressure?

   _____

2. What are two types of local winds?

   _____

3. Describe the movement of air over two nearby land areas, one of which is heated more than the other.

   _____

   _____

4. What causes local winds to form?

   _____

   _____

5. Identify where the sun's rays strike Earth most directly and least directly.

   _____

   _____

Building Vocabulary
In your notebook, write a definition for each of these terms.

6. wind

7. anemometer

8. windchill factor

9. sea breeze

10. Coriolis effect

CHAPTER 9 Review

Read each question and choose the best answer.

---

1 A group of students conduct an investigation to model and observe convection currents in Earth's atmosphere. They fill a pan with cool water to represent the atmosphere. They place drops of food coloring in the pan to represent local air regions. Then, they place a cup of hot water under the pan.

Pan filled with cool water

Hot water in cup

What does the hot water represent?

A Energy from wind currents

B Energy from ocean currents

C Energy from Earth's surface

D Energy from Earth's mantle

---

2 A student claims that local winds occur because the sun heats Earth's surface evenly, and this produces areas of high and low pressure in the air that cause wind to flow. What is wrong with this statement?

F The sun's energy is unrelated to high and low pressure in the air.

G The student described the process of global, not local, wind production.

H The student should have said that the sun heats Earth's surface unevenly.

J Wind only flows as a result of high pressure, not low pressure, air systems.

3 The graph shows the temperature of the atmosphere at different altitudes.

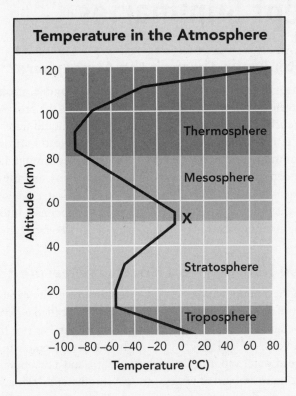

Temperature in the Atmosphere

What is responsible for the peak in the graph labeled X?

A Heat absorbed by atmospheric ozone

B Heat reflected by atmospheric clouds

C Heat re-radiated from Earth's surface

D Heat transferred from ocean currents

4 As you move from the troposphere to the stratosphere in Earth's atmosphere, which of the following statements is true?

F Air pressure decreases and air density decreases.

G Air pressure decreases and air density increases.

H Air pressure increases and air density decreases.

J Air pressure increases and air density increases.

 **10.1** **Water in the Atmosphere**

Key Concept Summaries

⬤ How Does Water Move Through the Atmosphere?

The sun drives the movement of water through Earth's systems; this movement is called the water cycle. **In the water cycle, water vapor enters the atmosphere by evaporation from the oceans and other bodies of water and leaves by precipitation or by condensation on the ground.** Liquid water from lakes and puddles undergoes evaporation —that is, molecules of liquid water escape into the air after becoming water vapor. Condensation is the reverse of evaporation; it is the process by which water vapor becomes liquid water. In the water cycle, precipitation falls to Earth where it runs off the surface or moves through the ground, flowing into lakes, streams, and the oceans. Water from these bodies of water evaporates, rises into the atmosphere, condenses into clouds. And the process starts all over again.

⬤ What Is Relative Humidity and How Is It Measured?

Humidity is a measure of the amount of water vapor in the air. The ability of air to hold water vapor depends on its temperature. Warm air can hold more water vapor than cool air. Relative humidity is the percentage of water vapor in the air as compared to the maximum amount of water vapor the air can hold at a particular temperature. For example, at 10°C, 1 cubic meter of air can hold at most 8 grams of water vapor. If the air had 4 grams of water vapor, the relative humidity would be 50 percent.

Relative humidity can be measured with an instrument called a psychrometer. A psychrometer has two thermometers, a wet-bulb thermometer, which is covered by a moist cloth, and a dry-bulb thermometer. When the psychrometer is "slung," or spun, air blows over both thermometers. Because the wet-bulb thermometer is cooled by evaporation, its reading drops. The relative humidity can be found by comparing the temperatures of the wet-bulb and dry-bulb thermometers.

10.1 Water in the Atmosphere

Review and Reinforce

Understanding Main Ideas

If the statement is true, write *true*. If the statement is false, change the underlined word or words to make the statement true.

1. _____ In the water cycle, water returns to Earth as <u>condensation</u>, usually in the form of rain or snow.

2. _____ During dry weather, the water level in a small pond drops because of <u>runoff</u>.

3. _____ In the water cycle, water vapor leaves the atmosphere by <u>condensation</u>.

4. _____ <u>Humidity</u> can be found by comparing the temperatures of wet-bulb and dry-bulb thermometers.

5. _____ Warm air can hold <u>more</u> water vapor than cool air.

Building Vocabulary

Write a definition for each of these terms on the lines below.

6. evaporation

_____

_____

7. humidity

_____

_____

8. psychrometer

_____

_____

_____

9. condensation

_____

_____

10. relative humidity

_____

_____

10.2 Clouds

Key Concept Summaries

🔑 How Do Clouds Form?

Clouds form when water vapor in the air condenses to form liquid water or ice crystals. Two conditions are required for condensation: cooling of the air and the presence of particles in the air. When air cools, water vapor in it condenses into tiny droplets of water. The temperature at which condensation begins is called the dew point. Before water vapor can condense and form clouds, it must have a surface on which to condense. These surfaces are small particles of dust, smoke, and salt crystals. Liquid water that condenses from the air onto a cooler surface is called dew. Ice deposited on a surface that is below freezing is called frost.

🔑 What Are the Three Main Types of Clouds?

Scientists classify clouds into three main types based on their shape: cirrus, cumulus, and stratus. Clouds are further classified by their altitude. Each type of cloud is associated with a different type of weather. Cirrus clouds are wispy and feathery. They form at high altitudes, usually above 6 km, and at low temperatures. Cirrus clouds are made of ice crystals and indicate fair weather. Cumulus clouds look like cotton. They form less than 2 km above the ground, but they may extend upward as much as 18 km. Short cumulus clouds usually indicate fair weather, but towering clouds with flat tops often produce thunderstorms. They are then called cumulonimbus clouds. (The suffix –*nimbus* means "rain.") Stratus clouds form in low, flat layers covering most or all of the sky. They are dull gray and may produce drizzle, rain, or snow. They are then called nimbostratus clouds.

Clouds are further classified by their altitude. Clouds that form between 2 and 6 km above Earth's surface have the prefix *alto-*, which means "high." Altocumulus and altostratus clouds are higher than regular cumulus and stratus clouds, but lower than cirrus clouds. Altocumulus and altostratus clouds indicate precipitation. Clouds that form near the ground are called fog.

Review and Reinforce

Understanding Main Ideas

Answer the following questions in the spaces provided.

1. Clouds form when water vapor in the air condenses to form _____

   _____

2. What two conditions are required for cloud formation? _____

   _____

3. Ice deposited by the atmosphere on a surface that is below freezing is called

   _____.

4. _____ clouds are fluffy, towering clouds with flat tops that
   often produce thunderstorms.

5. Describe altostratus clouds. _____

   _____

6. Fog is the name for _____.

Building Vocabulary

Match each term with its definition by writing the letter of the correct definition in
the right column on the line beside the term in the left column.

7. _____ dew point

8. _____ cirrus

9. _____ cumulus

10. _____ stratus

a. whispy, feathery clouds that form at
high altitudes

b. the temperature at which condensation
begins

c. clouds that form in flat layers close to the
ground

d. clouds that look like cotton and form less
than 2 km above the ground

10.3 Precipitation

Key Concept Summaries

🔑 What Are the Common Types of Precipitation?

Any form of water that falls from clouds and reaches Earth's surface is precipitation. **Common types of precipitation include rain, sleet, freezing rain, snow, and hail.** Rain is the most common. Drops of water are called rain if they are at least 0.5 millimeters in diameter. Smaller drops of water are called drizzle, and even smaller ones are called mist. An open-ended can or tube that collects rainfall is called a rain gauge.

There are four types of freezing precipitation: freezing rain, snow, sleet, and hail. Freezing rain is rain that freezes when it hits a cold surface. When clouds are colder, water vapor can convert directly into ice crystals, forming snow. When raindrops fall through a layer of air colder than 0°C, they can freeze into ice particles. Ice particles smaller than 5 millimeters in diameter are called sleet. Round pellets of ice larger than 5 mm in diameter are called hailstones. Hail forms only inside cumulonimbus clouds during thunderstorms. It forms when strong updrafts repeatedly carry ice pellets through cold regions of a cloud, adding another layer of ice each time.

🔑 What Are the Causes and Effects of Floods and Droughts?

A flood is an overflowing of water in a normally dry area. **Small or large, many floods occur when the volume of water in a river increases so much that the river overflows its channel.** Over a brief time period, heavy rains or melting snow can cause a river to overflow, uprooting trees and even destroying bridges and buildings. People try to control floods by building dams across rivers and levees.

A long period of scarce rainfall or dry weather is known as a drought. Because it reduces the supplies of groundwater and surface water, a drought can cause a shortage of water for homes and businesses. **Droughts are usually caused by dry weather systems that remain in one place for weeks or months at a time.** Long-term droughts can cause crop failure and even famine. People can prepare for droughts by conserving water when dry conditions first occur. Farmers can grow drought-resistant plants that have been bred to withstand dry conditions.

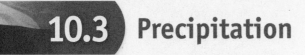

10.3 Precipitation

Review and Reinforce

Understanding Main Ideas

Fill in the blanks in the table below.

Types of Precipitation	Description
1.	Water droplets at least 0.5 millimeters in diameter
Sleet	2.
3.	Rain that freezes on a cold surface
Hail	4.
5.	Water vapor condensed directly to ice crystals within a cloud

Building Vocabulary

Write a definition for each of these terms on the lines below.

6. precipitation

_____

_____

7. rain gauge

_____

_____

8. flood

_____

_____

9. drought

_____

_____

10.4 Air Masses

Key Concept Summaries

What Are the Major Air Masses?

An air mass is a huge body of air in the lower atmosphere that has similar temperature, humidity, and air pressure at any given height. **Four major types of air masses influence the weather in North America: maritime tropical, continental tropical, maritime polar, and continental polar.** Maritime air masses form over the ocean and can be very humid. Continental air masses form over land, and are drier than maritime air masses. Tropical air masses are warm, form in the tropics, and have low air pressure. Polar air masses are cold, form near the poles, and have high air pressure. In North America, most air masses move from west to east. Jet streams are bands of high-speed winds about 10 kilometers above the surface of Earth that push air masses along. Fronts occur along the boundaries between air masses. Changeable weather develops along fronts.

What Are the Main Types of Fronts?

Colliding air masses can form four types of fronts: cold fronts, warm fronts, stationary fronts, and occluded fronts. When a faster cold air mass runs into a slower warm air mass, a cold front forms. The cold air slides under the warm air. As the warm air rises, it cools and condenses, often resulting in heavy rain or snow. When a faster warm air mass runs into a slower cold air mass, a warm front forms. The warm air slides up over the cold air, possibly causing light rain or snow. When a cold air mass and warm air mass collide, but neither displaces the other, a stationary front occurs. Water vapor in the warm air condenses into rain, snow, fog, or clouds, lingering for days. When a warm air mass is caught between two cooler air masses, the warm air is pushed up and an occluded front forms. The warm air mass is cut off, or occluded, from the ground. Temperatures at the ground get cooler, and it may get cloudy and rain or snow.

What Weather Do Cyclones and Anticyclones Bring?

A swirling center of low-pressure air is called a cyclone. In the Northern Hemisphere, cyclones spin counterclockwise when viewed from above. **Cyclones and decreasing air pressure are associated with clouds, wind, and precipitation.** An anticyclone is the opposite of a cyclone. **The descending air in an anticyclone generally causes dry, clear weather.**

Air Masses

Review and Reinforce

Understanding Main Ideas

Fill in the blanks in the table below.

Type of Air Mass	Where It Forms	Temperature	Humidity
1.	Over ocean	Warm	Moist
Maritime polar	2.	Cold	Moist
Continental tropical	Over land	3.	Dry
Continental polar	Over land	Cold	4.

Building Vocabulary

Write a definition for each of these terms on the lines below.

5. air mass

_____

_____

6. front

_____

7. jet stream

_____

_____

8. occluded front

_____

_____

9. cyclone

_____

10. anticyclone

_____

10.5 Storms

Key Concept Summaries

🔑 How Do the Different Types of Storms Form?

A storm is a violent disturbance in the atmosphere. Storms involve sudden changes in air pressure, which cause rapid air movements. Winter storms, thunderstorms, hurricanes, and tornadoes are all types of severe storms. Winter storms involve snow. **All year round, most precipitation begins in clouds as snow. If the air is colder than 0°C all the way to the ground, the precipitation falls as snow.** A thunderstorm is a small storm often accompanied by heavy precipitation and frequent thunder and lightning. **Thunderstorms form in large cumulonimbus clouds, also known as thunderheads.** Lightning is a sudden spark, or electrical discharge, that jumps between parts of a cloud, between nearby clouds, or between a cloud and the ground. A hurricane is a tropical cyclone with winds of 119 km/h or higher. **A hurricane begins over warm ocean water as a low-pressure area, or tropical disturbance.** The low pressure and winds of a hurricane can cause storm surge, a "dome" of water that sweeps across the coast where the hurricane lands. A tornado is a rapidly spinning column of air that reaches down from a thunderstorm to touch Earth's surface. **Tornadoes most commonly develop in thick cumulonimbus clouds—the same clouds that bring thunderstorms.**

🔑 How Can You Stay Safe in a Storm?

If you are caught in a snowstorm, try to find shelter from the wind. If you are in a car, be sure the exhaust pipe is free of snow before you run the engine. **During thunderstorms, avoid places where lightning may strike. Also, avoid objects that can conduct electricity, such as metal objects and bodies of water.** In case of a hurricane, you should be prepared to evacuate, or move away temporarily. **If you hear a hurricane warning and are told to evacuate, leave the area immediately. The safest place to be during a tornado is in a storm shelter or a basement.** If there is no basement, move to the middle of the ground floor away from windows and doors.

10.5 Storms

Review and Reinforce

Understanding Main Ideas

Answer the following questions in the spaces provided. Use a separate sheet of paper if you need more room.

1. Why should you be on the lookout for tornadoes during a severe thunderstorm? _____

_____

2. Why should you avoid touching metal objects during a thunderstorm? _____

_____

3. What causes thunder? _____

_____

4. Why does a hurricane lose strength as it passes over land? _____

_____

5. Where is the safest place to be during a tornado? _____

_____

Building Vocabulary

Match each term with its definition by writing the letter of the correct definition in the right column on the line beside the term in the left column.

6. _____ thunderstorm

7. _____ tornado

8. _____ hurricane

9. _____ storm surge

10. _____ evacuate

a. a tropical storm that has winds of 119 km/h or greater

b. a small storm accompanied by heavy precipitation and frequent thunder and lightning

c. a rapidly spinning column of air that reaches from a storm cloud to Earth

d. move away temporarily

e. a dome of water that sweeps across the coast where a hurricane lands

 **10.6** Predicting Local Weather

Key Concept Summaries

🔑 How Do You Predict the Weather?

The first step in forecasting is to collect data. This can be done either through direct observations, such as recognizing that cumulonimbus clouds may produce a thunderstorm, or through the use of instruments such as a barometer. Meteorologists are scientists who study and try to predict the weather. **Meteorologists use maps, charts, computers, and other technology to analyze weather data and to prepare weather forecasts.**

Weather reporters get their information from the National Weather Service, which uses weather balloons, satellites, radar, and surface instruments to gather data. Weather balloons carry instruments into the troposphere and lower stratosphere to measure temperature, air pressure, and humidity. Satellites in the exosphere, the uppermost layer of the atmosphere, collect data on temperature, humidity, solar radiation, and wind speed and direction. They also include cameras that can make images of clouds, storms, and snow cover. Automated weather stations in 1,700 surface locations gather data on temperature, air pressure, relative humidity, rainfall, and wind speed and direction. Computers help process all of this weather data quickly to help forecasters make predictions. Currently, forecasts are fairly accurate up to five days in the future.

🔑 What Can You Learn From Weather Maps?

The National Weather Service maintains weather maps that are snapshots of conditions at a particular time over a large area. Some show curved lines that connect places where certain conditions are the same. Isobars (*iso* meaning "equal" and *bar* meaning "weight") are lines joining places on the map that have the same air pressure. Isotherms are lines joining places that have the same temperature. **Standard symbols on weather maps show fronts, areas of high and low pressure, types of precipitation, and temperatures.**

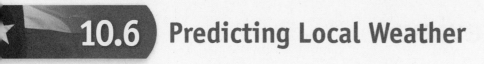

10.6 Predicting Local Weather

Review and Reinforce

Understanding Main Ideas

Fill in the blanks in the table.

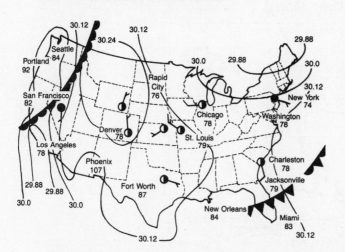

Weather Factor	Denver	Chicago	New York
Temperature (°F)	78	**1.**	74
Cloud Cover	**2.**	partly cloudy	cloudy
Wind direction	**3.**	From the west	From the southeast
Wind speed (mph)	3–8	9–14	**4.**
Air pressure (inches)	30.3	**5.**	30.0

Building Vocabulary

In your notebook, write a definition for each of these terms.

6. meteorologists

7. isobars

8. isotherms

Write About It

9. In your notebook, describe the kinds of weather data meteorologists receive from weather balloons, satellites, and automated weather stations.

Read each question and choose the best answer.

1 The map shows the weather conditions in North America on a certain day.

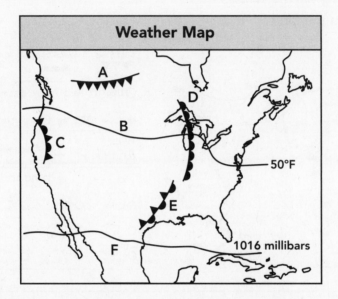

Weather Map

50°F

1016 millibars

Which location on the map will most likely experience cool, dry conditions?

A Location A

B Location B

C Location C

D Location D

2 Which of the following would be the relative humidity reading for air that is at its dew point temperature?

F 0%

G 50%

H 100%

J 150%

3 Hurricane Lili struck the United States in 2002. The estimated average wind speed of the hurricane from September 21 to October 5 is shown below.

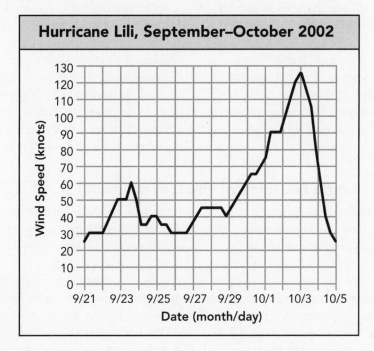

On which day did the hurricane most likely make landfall?

A September 24

B September 29

C October 3

D October 5

4 Which of the following are essential components in the formation of a hurricane?

F Low pressure, warm temperature, ocean waters, spiraling winds

G High pressure, cool temperature, strong winds, humid air

H High pressure, high temperaure, cyclonic winds, dry air

J Warm front, clouds, low pressure, high elevation

11.1 Exploring the Ocean

Key Concept Summaries

🗝 How Do Conditions Vary in Earth's Oceans?

The water in Earth's oceans varies in salinity, temperature, and depth. Salinity is the total amount of dissolved salts in a sample of water. Salinity affects the temperature and density of water. Saltwater freezes at a lower temperature and has a higher density than freshwater.

Like temperatures on land, temperatures at the surface of the ocean vary with location and the seasons. The temperature drops as you travel away from the equator. **As you descend through the ocean, the water temperature decreases.** There are three temperature zones in the water column: the surface zone, the transition zone, and the deep zone.

Water pressure, the force exerted by the weight of water, also changes with depth. **In the ocean, pressure increases by 1 bar, the air pressure at sea level, with each 10 meters of depth.**

🗝 What Are Some Features of the Ocean Floor?

Scientists have developed technology to study the ocean floor. A major advance in ocean-floor mapping was sonar, sound navigation and ranging. This system uses sound waves to calculate the distance to an object.

Major ocean floor features include trenches, the continental shelf, the continental slope, the abyssal plain, and the mid-ocean ridge. These features have all been formed by the interaction of Earth's plates.

A seamount is a volcanic mountain rising from the ocean floor. Mid-ocean ridges are long chains of mountains on the ocean floor. The continental shelf is a gently sloping shallow area that extends outward from the edge of each continent. The steep edge of the continental shelf is called the continental slope. The abyssal plain is a broad area covered with thick layers of mud and silt. A trench is a long, deep valley on the ocean floor through which old ocean floor sinks back toward the mantle.

11.1 Exploring the Ocean

Review and Reinforce

Understanding Main Ideas

Fill in the spaces in the table below.

The Ocean Water Column		
Depth Zone	Depth Range	Average Temperature (°C)
Surface	0 to 500 m	1.
Transition	2.	4.0
3.	1 km and deeper	3.5

Answer the following questions in your notebook.

4. What are three ways in which ocean water varies?

5. Which condition of ocean water varies with the location and seasons?

6. How does water temperature change as you move from the ocean floor to the surface?

7. What prevents scuba divers from going deeper than 40 meters below the surface?

8. How do ocean floor features such as trenches and mid-ocean ridges form?

Building Vocabulary

In your notebook, write a definition for each of these terms.

9. continental shelf

10. salinity

11. trench

12. sonar

13. continental slope

14. mid-ocean ridge

15. abyssal plain

16. seamount

Key Concept Summaries

🔑 What Causes Surface Currents?

A current is a large stream of moving water that flows through the oceans. Unlike waves, currents carry water from one place to another. **Surface currents follow Earth's global wind patterns and are driven mainly by winds. Global winds, in turn, are caused by differences in the amount of solar energy that strikes different parts of Earth's surface. Thus, the sun provides the energy that drives the surface currents.**

As Earth rotates, the paths of winds and currents curve. This effect of Earth's rotation on the direction of winds and currents is called the Coriolis effect.

The Gulf Stream is the largest and most powerful surface current in the North Atlantic Ocean. It has a warming effect on the climate of nearby land areas. Climate is the pattern of temperature and precipitation typical of an area over a long period of time. **A surface current warms or cools the air above it. This affects the climate of land near the coast.**

Changes in wind patterns and currents can have a major impact on the oceans and nearby land. One example of such changes is El Niño, a climate event that occurs every two to seven years in the Pacific Ocean. When El Niño occurs, unusual wind patterns cause a vast sheet of warm water to move east toward South America. When surface waters in the eastern Pacific are colder than normal, a climate event known as La Niña occurs.

🔑 What Causes Deep Currents?

Deep currents are caused by differences in the density of ocean water. When a surface current moves toward the poles, its water temperature decreases and its salinity increases. **As the temperature of the water near the poles decreases and its salinity increases, the water becomes denser and sinks. Then, the cold, dense water flows back along the ocean floor as a deep current.** Deep currents move and mix water around the world. They carry cold water from the poles toward the equator.

The pattern of ocean currents looks like a conveyor belt, moving water between the oceans. **The sun's energy warms the ocean's surface and the atmosphere near the equator more than near the poles. The resulting temperature differences in ocean water, along with differences in salinity, drive convection within the ocean, producing deep currents.**

11.2 Currents and Climate

Review and Reinforce

Understanding Main Ideas

Fill in the spaces in the table below.

Type of Current	Cause
1.	Winds
Deep	2.

Answer the following questions in the spaces provided.

3. How do surface currents affect climate?

_____

_____

4. How do deep currents affect the oceans?

_____

_____

_____

Building Vocabulary

Fill in the blank to complete each statement.

5. _____ is a climate event that occurs when surface waters in the eastern Pacific are colder than normal.

6. _____ is an abnormal climate event that occurs every 2 to 7 years in the Pacific Ocean.

7. _____ are large streams of moving water that flow through the oceans.

8. _____ is the pattern of temperature and precipitation typical of an area over a long period of time.

 ## Write About It

9. In your notebook, contrast the two main types of ocean currents and their causes.

Key Concept Summaries

What Are the Ocean's Living and Nonliving Resources?

People use products made from living and nonliving resources in the ocean. **People depend on ocean organisms for food. Ocean organisms also provide materials that are used in products such as detergents and paints.** Fisheries renew themselves naturally each year, but overfishing has caused a shortage of fish in some areas. Aquaculture, the farming of salt- and freshwater organisms, is increasingly common. Algae is harvested for use in many products. **Some nonliving ocean resources include water, fuels, and minerals.** Water can be extracted from the ocean and, in a process called desalination, treated to remove salt. Fuels such as oil and natural gas have been created naturally over the course of hundreds of millions of years out of the remains of dead marine organisms. Minerals and metals accumulate on the ocean floor. The metals concentrate around pieces of shell, forming black lumps called nodules. Minerals and nutrients are brought to the surface of the ocean as a result of upwelling, the movement of cold water upward from the deep ocean.

What Are the Sources of Ocean Pollution?

The ocean cleans itself naturally. However, the ocean cannot absorb large amounts of wastes, and so many marine organisms are threatened by the dumping of such wastes. **Although some ocean pollution is the result of natural occurrences, most pollution is related to human activities.** Some pollution is caused by weather such as heavy rains. Yet sewage, chemicals, and trash are dumped into coastal waters by humans. Other substances that run off fields and roads can end up in the ocean. Oil pollution from damaged tankers or drilling platforms can cause wide destruction to living things in the ocean. Because the world ocean is a continuous body of water with no boundaries, nations must cooperate to protect it.

11.3 **Ocean Resources**

Review and Reinforce

Understanding Main Ideas

Use the table below to answer Questions 1–3.

Total Catch (in metric tons)		
Fish Species	**1970**	**1993**
Haddock	829,300	226,500
Atlantic cod	2,817,500	1,028,700
Peruvian anchovy	11,845,300	7,464,600

1. How did the catches of these three fish species change in the period shown?

   _____

2. Why do you think these changes might have occurred?

   _____

3. What can be done to protect fish populations?

   _____

Answer the following questions in the space provided.

4. What happens to the remains of dead marine organisms to transform them into oil and gas?

   _____

   _____

5. Why must nations cooperate to reduce ocean pollution?

   _____

   _____

Building Vocabulary

Write a definition for each of these terms.

6. upwelling _____

7. nodules _____

CHAPTER 11 Review

Read each question and choose the best answer.

1 The diagram below shows a simplified pattern of global ocean convection currents at the surface and in the deep ocean.

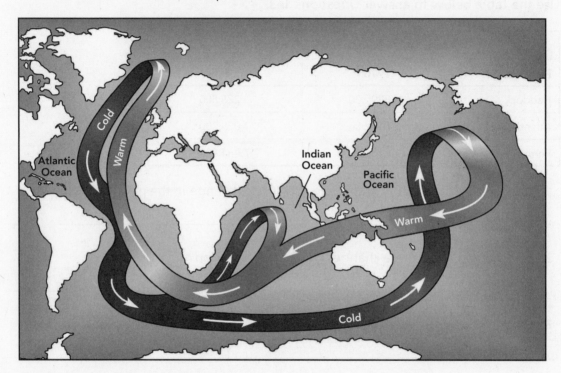

How does energy from the sun contribute to these currents?

A It causes cold water to sink down in the ocean at the poles.

B It causes the Coriolis effect, which curves the currents around the continents.

C It causes the wind currents that determine the path of the cold ocean currents.

D It heats the warm surface currents that transfer heat from the equator to the polar regions.

2 A group of students lists resources that are important in their community on the following flipchart.

Resources Used By Our Community

fresh water
sea salt
paper
wheat
natural gas

Which resources can be obtained either directly or indirectly from the ocean?

F Paper, wheat, sea salt

G Natural gas, paper, wheat

H Paper, fresh water, sea salt

J Fresh water, sea salt, natural gas

3 Ocean currents transfer the sun's energy to different locations on Earth. Which of the following best explains the primary method by which thermal energy from the ocean is transferred to the land?

A Ocean waves strike the coast and conduct thermal energy.

B Deep ocean currents rise up to the ocean surface and cool coastal locations.

C Ocean water changes the temperature of the air above it.

D Low-pressure systems over the ocean form cyclonic storms that move over landmasses.

12.1 Ecosystems

Key Concept Summaries

How Are Ecosystems Organized?

An ecosystem is all the things that live in a particular area, along with their nonliving environment. The parts of an ecosystem that are living or were once living are called biotic factors. The nonliving parts of an ecosystem are called abiotic factors. Sunlight, soil, water, oxygen, and temperature are all abiotic factors. An organism's habitat is the environment that provides the things an organism needs to live, grow, and reproduce. **An ecosystem's levels of organization are organism, population, community, and ecosystem.** All members of one species that live in the area make up a population. All of the populations that live together in a particular area form a community.

What Are the Energy Roles of Organisms in Ecosystems?

All organisms have an energy role in their ecosystem. **The energy role an organism plays in its ecosystem is that of a producer, a consumer, or a decomposer.** An organism that makes its own food is called a producer. Plants, phytoplankton, and algae are producers. An organism that feeds on other organisms to obtain energy is called a consumer. Consumers are classified by the type of food they eat.

Herbivores get their energy by eating only plants. Omnivores eat plants and animals. Carnivores eat only animals. A scavenger is a carnivore that feeds on the bodies of dead or decaying organisms. A decomposer is an organism that gets energy by breaking down biotic wastes and dead organisms, returning the raw materials to soil and water. Fungi, such as mushrooms, and bacteria are all decomposers.

How Does Energy Flow in Ecosystems?

Energy flows through an ecosystem when one organism eats another. Food chains and food webs are ways to model how energy flows in an ecosystem. A food chain is a series of events in an ecosystem in which organisms transfer energy by eating and being eaten. A food chain always begins with a producer. A food web is a model that shows the overlapping feeding relationships, or food chains, in an ecosystem.

12.1 Ecosystems

Review and Reinforce

Understanding Main Ideas

Fill in the blank to complete each statement.

1. A consumer that eats only animals is called a _____.

2. A _____ in an ecosystem can make its own food.

3. A _____ can show all the feeding relationships in an ecosystem.

4. Mushrooms and bacteria are _____.

5. _____ factors in an ecosystem could include water and soil.

Building Vocabulary

In your notebook, write a definition for each of these terms.

6. food chain

7. scavenger

8. ecosystem

9. population

10. herbivore

11. biotic factors

12. consumer

13. habitat

Write About It

14. In your notebook, make a food chain that includes an eagle, algae, a small fish, and a large fish.

Key Concept Summaries

🔑 How Do Populations Change in Size?

Populations can change in size when new members join the population or when members leave the population. The birth rate counts the number of births in a population over a certain amount of time. The death rate counts the number of deaths in a population over a certain amount of time.

When the birth rate is greater than the death rate, the population will generally increase. The population will generally decrease when the death rate is greater than the birth rate. For example, the white-tailed deer population in Iowa decreased due to over-hunting.

The population can also change when individuals move into or out of the population. Immigration means moving into a population and emigration means leaving a population. Ecologists can graph how a population changes over time. The population density is the number of individuals in an area of a specific size.

🔑 What Factors Limit Population Growth?

A limiting factor is something in the environment that keeps a population from growing or makes a population smaller. **Some limiting factors for populations are climate, space, food, and water.**

Climate changes and unusual weather events, such as tornados, can limit population growth. The amount of available space can also limit population growth. For example, a plant needs to grow in a large enough space to obtain the things it needs to survive. Food and water are also often limiting factors when they are in limited supply.

Limiting factors determine an area's carrying capacity. Carrying capacity is the largest population that an area can support.

12.2 Populations

Review and Reinforce

Understanding Main Ideas

Answer the following questions in your notebook.

1. A vegetable garden is 12 meters long by 7 meters wide. It is home to 168 mice. What is the population density of the mice?

2. What are two ways that the size of a population can increase? What are two ways that the size of a population can decrease?

3. Identify three limiting factors that can prevent a population from increasing. Explain how each factor limits a population's size.

The line graph below shows how the size of the squirrel population in a city park changed over time. Use the line graph to answer questions 4–6.

4. Over which time period(s) did the squirrel population increase?

5. Over which time period(s) did the squirrel population decrease?

6. In which year did the population reach its lowest point? What was the size of the population that year?

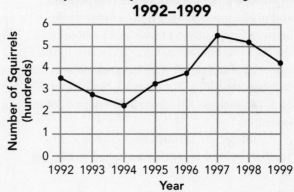

Building Vocabulary

Fill in the blank to complete each statement.

7. Moving into a population is called _____.

8. Moving out of a population is called _____.

9. The largest _____ an area can support is called the carrying capacity.

10. The number of individuals that die in a population in a certain time period is the _____.

Write About It

11. In your notebook, explain how space is a limiting factor for plants.

 **12.3** Interactions Among Living Things

Key Concept Summaries

🔑 How Do Adaptations Help an Organism Survive?

Individuals with characteristics that are best suited for their environment tend to survive and pass on these characteristics to their offspring through a process called natural selection. The behaviors and physical characteristics that allow organisms to live successfully in their environments are called adaptations. Individuals with characteristics that are poorly suited for their environment are less likely to survive and reproduce.

An organism has a role, or niche, in its habitat. A niche includes the type of food the organism eats, how it gets this food, and what other organisms eat it. A niche also includes when and how the organism reproduces and the physical conditions that it needs to survive. **Every organism has a variety of adaptations that are suited to its specific living conditions and help it survive.**

🔑 What Are Competition and Predation?

Two major types of interactions among organisms and populations are competition and predation. Competition is the struggle between organisms to survive as they attempt to use the same limited resources. Populations that share the same habitat often have adaptations that reduce competition. For example, three types of birds can each get food from different parts of the same tree.

An interaction is which one organism kills another for food or nutrients is called predation.

The predator organism kills the prey organism. Predators have adaptations that help them catch prey. Organisms have adaptations that help them avoid becoming prey.

Predators can affect population size. If too many predators live in an area, the number of prey will decrease. As a result, there is less food for predators and the predator population will decrease as well.

🔑 What Are the Three Types of Symbiosis?

Symbiosis is any relationship in which two species live closely together and at least one of the species benefits. **The three main types of symbiotic relationships are mutualism, commensalism, and parasitism.** Mutualism is a relationship in which both species benefit. When an oxpecker eats ticks living on the impala's ear, both organisms benefit. Commensalism is a

relationship in which one species benefits and the other species is not affected, such as a bird's nest in a tree. Parasitism is a relationship that involves one organism living with, on, or inside another organism and harming it. The organism that benefits is called a parasite. The organism that it lives on or in is called the host.

12.3 Interactions Among Living Things

Review and Reinforce

Understanding Main Ideas

Answer the following questions in your notebook.

1. How does natural selection result in adaptations in a species?

2. What is an organism's niche?

3. How do adaptations help an organism to reduce competition for food and other resources?

The line graph below shows how the populations of lynx and snowshoe hares has changed over time. Use the line graph to answer questions 4–6.

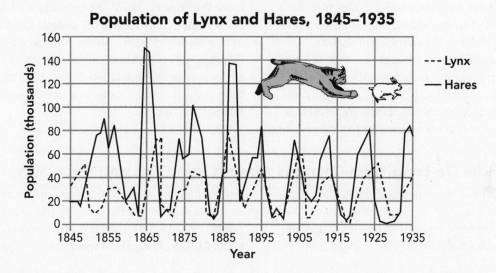

Population of Lynx and Hares, 1845–1935

4. When the hare population increased, what happened to the lynx population? Why?

5. How do you think an increase in the lynx population affected the hare population? Why?

6. What other factors could have caused a decrease in the hare population?

Building Vocabulary

In your notebook, write a definition for each of these terms.

7. predator

8. competition

9. symbiosis

12.4 Organisms, Populations, and Change

Key Concept Summaries

🔑 How Do Populations Become Adapted to Their Environments?

Organisms have a variety of traits, or characteristics. Traits are adaptations if they allow an organism to live in a certain environment. The sequence of DNA that determines a trait and is passed from parent to offspring is called a gene. A gene may have different forms, or alleles, that code for variations of the trait it determines. The alleles that an organism inherits from its parents determine the organism's traits. Alleles that code for adaptations are sometimes called favorable alleles. **A population adapts to its environment by the spread of favorable alleles.**

🔑 How Do Short-term Changes Affect Organisms and Populations?

A short-term environmental change usually occurs suddenly and lasts for a relatively short period of time. The changing of seasons, floods, storms, and drought can cause short-term environmental changes. Short-term environmental changes can affect organisms and populations. **Short-term environmental changes may cause organisms to stop growing, leave the area, or die. Short-term changes in an environment may reduce the genetic diversity of populations that live there.** The genetic diversity of a population is the variation in alleles within the population. Some populations have developed adaptations that make use of the periodic change.

🔑 How Do Long-term Changes Affect Organisms and Populations?

Long-term environmental changes often occur gradually and last for many thousands of years. Geologic processes, climate change, and gradual habitat destruction can cause long-term environmental change. **Organisms may emigrate or die during long-term changes. Subsequent populations may disappear or develop useful traits for the changed environment.**

12.4 Organisms, Populations, and Change

Review and Reinforce

Understanding Main Ideas

Fill in the blank to complete each statement.

1. _____ environmental changes can quickly affect both individual organisms and populations.

2. Only organisms that _____ environmental change can pass on their alleles to offspring.

3. Climate change can bring about _____ environmental changes.

4. Alleles determine the _____ of an organism.

5. Populations _____ when organisms with favorable alleles survive and pass those alleles to offspring.

Building Vocabulary

Write a definition for each of these terms on the lines below.

6. alleles

_____

_____

7. gene

_____

_____

8. genetic diversity

_____

_____

Write About It

9. In your notebook, describe how a population of pond grasses could become adapted to frequent flooding.

CHAPTER 12 Review

Read each question and choose the best answer.

---

1 Prior to the Industrial Revolution, most of the population of a species of moth were white with black spots. The moths lived on the bark of white trees in London. During the Industrial Revolution, air pollution increased. Many trees were covered in dark soot, as shown. After several generations, the population of moths changed. Eventually, most of the moths were darker.

Which of the following best explains what caused this to happen?

A Moths with darker colors were more likely to be eaten by birds.

B Moths began to transfer only the genes for black coloring to their offspring.

C Darker moths were more likely to survive, so their genes spread through the population.

D Moths developed black specks so that they could blend in with the trees more easily.

---

2 A family notices that their dog has fleas. The fleas bite and consume the blood of the dog, causing it to itch. Which of the following best describes the relationship between the dog and the fleas?

F The dog and fleas have a predator/prey relationship.

G The dog and fleas have a consumer/producer relationship.

H The dog and fleas have a parasite/host relationship.

J The dog and fleas have an abiotic/biotic relationship.

3 A student draws a flow chart to model the parasite-host relationship between a *Sacculina* barnacle and a crab in a marine ecosystem.

The *Sacculina* finds a joint in a female crab's shell and attaches to the crab's soft body.

The *Sacculina* obtains energy and nutrients from the crab's blood.

The *Sacculina* lays its eggs.

?

Which phrase correctly completes the chart?

A The crab eats the eggs to replenish the nutrients that it lost from the *Sacculina*.

B The crab nurtures the eggs, which hatch, grow, and spread through the habitat.

C The crab's own eggs become fertilized in this process.

D The crab uses the eggs to feed its offspring.

4 An ecologist studies a population of bees. He notices that the size of the population varies when certain conditions in the environment change. An increase in which of the following would most likely result in a decrease in the bee population?

F Competitors

G Food supply

H Shelter

J Water supply

Grade 6 and 7 Supporting TEKS Review

Review these Grade 6 and 7 Supporting TEKS to prepare for the Texas Grade 8 Assessment.

TEKS 6.5C Differentiate between elements and compounds on the most basic level.

An element and a chemical compound are both pure substances. An element is a substance that cannot be broken down into other substances by chemical means. Elements are made of only one type of atom. For example, iron is an element. An atom of iron (Fe) is the smallest particle of iron that still has the properties of iron. It cannot be broken down into any other substances. However, one or more atoms of iron can combine chemically with other atoms to form a molecule that has properties different from those of its individual elements. A chemical compound is a substance made of two or more elements that are chemically combined in a set ratio. For example, two atoms of iron can combine with three atoms of oxygen (O) to make one molecule of a chemical compound called iron oxide, or Fe_2O_3. Iron oxide is rust.

TEKS Review Question

Sodium is a non-poisonous silvery-white solid. Chlorine is a deadly greenish-yellow gas. When they combine, they form sodium chloride, or table salt. Which of the following statements describes why this occurs?

A Chlorine occurs in diatomic form, or Cl_2, in nature.

B The elements in a compound join physically.

C A chemical compound keeps the properties of its individual elements.

D A chemical compound has properties unlike those of its individual elements.

TEKS 6.6A Compare metals, nonmetals, and metalloids using physical properties such as luster, conductivity, or malleability.

A physical property of a substance is a characteristic that can be observed and measured. Most metals, for example, have luster, or shininess. They also have conductivity, meaning they allow heat and electricity to move through them easily. Most metals can be hammered into thin sheets, making them malleable. The physical properties of nonmetals are almost opposite those of metals. Most nonmetals are gases at room temperature, so they have no luster. Nonmetals are also poor conductors and are brittle in their solid form instead of malleable. Metalloids have properties of both metals and nonmetals.

TEKS Review Question

Which element in the chart is a metalloid?

Element	Physical Property
Aluminum	solid, highly malleable, good conductor
Boron	shiny, poor conductor at room temperatures, good conductor at higher temperatures
Carbon	poor conductor, not malleable
Lead	dark gray, highly malleable, poor conductor

F Aluminum

G Boron

H Carbon

J Lead

TEKS 6.6B Calculate density to identify an unknown substance.

Density is a physical property of matter. Each element has a specific density measurement, which makes it a useful characteristic for identifying unknown substances. Density is a ratio of an object's mass to its volume. Mass is the amount of matter in an object, and volume is the amount of space an object or substance takes up. In SI, the basic unit for density is kg/m^3. It is also often measured in g/cm^3 or g/mL.

$$\text{Density} = \frac{\text{Mass (kg)}}{\text{Volume (m}^3\text{)}}$$

TEKS Review Question

Pure aluminum has a density of 2.7 g/cm^3. Which of the samples in the table is most likely aluminum?

Sample	Mass (g)	Volume (cm³)
1	10.6	5.3
2	6.0	16.2
3	5.4	2.0
4	5.7	3.0

A Sample 1

B Sample 2

C Sample 3

D Sample 4

TEKS 6.8A Compare and contrast potential and kinetic energy.

Potential energy (PE) is stored energy that results from an object's position. Potential energy that is related to an object's height is called gravitational potential energy. The potential energy at a certain height equals the work that would be required to lift the object to that height. The force you use to lift the object is equal to its weight.

$$\text{Gravitational potential energy} = \text{Weight} \times \text{Height}$$

Kinetic energy is energy based on an object's motion. The kinetic energy of an object depends on its speed and mass. The faster an object moves, the more kinetic energy it has. Also, if two objects are moving at the same speed, the object with the greater mass has more kinetic energy.

$$\text{Kinetic energy} = \frac{1}{2} \times \text{Mass} \times \text{Speed}^2$$

TEKS Review Question

A ball starts from rest and rolls down a hill. Which of the following statements about the ball's kinetic and potential energy is true?

F The ball's kinetic energy is highest and potential energy lowest at the top of the hill.

G The ball's kinetic energy is lowest and potential energy highest at the top of the hill.

H The ball's kinetic and potential energy are highest at the top of the hill.

J The ball's kinetic and potential energy are lowest at the top of the hill.

Grade 6 and 7 Supporting TEKS Review *continued*

🔻 TEKS 6.8C Calculate average speed using distance and time measurements.

An object's speed depends on two factors: distance traveled and elapsed time. The distance traveled is measured in units of length, such as kilometers. Time is measured in units such as minutes. The relationship between the distance and the time it takes to travel that distance is speed and can be expressed as a ratio:

$$\text{Speed} = \frac{\text{Distance}}{\text{Time}}$$

The speed at which most moving objects travel is not constant. A moving object's speed may vary during the distance traveled, but the object has an average speed over the distance traveled. The object's average speed can be expressed as a ratio. To calculate average speed, divide the total distance traveled by the total time.

$$\text{Average speed} = \frac{\text{Total distance}}{\text{Total time}}$$

🔻 TEKS Review Question

A hiker has recorded the distance and time for each of his last four hikes. What is his average speed?

Hike	Distance (in km)	Time (in hours)
1	9	3
2	10	4
3	7	2
4	16	5

A 2 kilometers per hour

B 3 kilometers per hour

C 4 kilometers per hour

D 5 kilometers per hour

🔻 TEKS 6.8D Measure and graph changes in motion.

Motion is a change in position measured by distance and time. Changes in motion can be represented in graphs, called distance-versus-time graphs. Time is plotted along the x-axis. Distance is plotted along the y-axis.

Straight lines on a motion graph represent constant speed. Lines that curve upward show an increase in speed. The steeper the graphed line, the faster an object's motion. Lines that curve downward represent decreasing speed. Horizontal lines show no change in position, meaning the object is at rest.

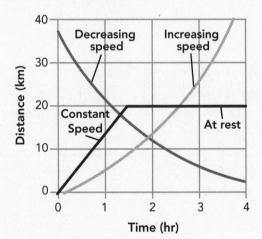

🔻 TEKS Review Question

A bike race begins. A rider pedals at an increasing rate for three hours on a flat course before becoming overheated. The rider waits by the side of the road until help arrives. What would the line on a distance v. time graph of the rider's motion look?

F A straight line for the distance covered in three hours

G A line that curves upward for three hours and then becomes horizontal

H A line that curves upward for three hours and then curves downward

J A line that curves downward for three hours and then becomes horizontal

⚜ TEKS 6.9C Demonstrate energy transformations such as energy in a flashlight battery changes from chemical energy to electrical energy to light energy.

Energy can be transformed from one kind to another. For example, a diver standing at the edge of a diving board has gravitational potential energy. That potential energy changes, or is transformed, into kinetic energy as the diver dives from the board and enters the water. Energy transformations occur between other kinds of energy, too. The chemical energy in a battery, for example, is transformed into electrical energy when a flashlight is turned on. Electrical energy is then transformed into light energy that you can see and thermal energy that you can feel.

⚜ TEKS Review Question

The kinetic energy of wind transfers to the blades of a wind turbine, making them turn. As the blades spin, the shaft to which they are attached rotates. The rotating shaft powers a generator, or a set of magnets surrounding a coil of wire. An electric current forms in the wire and flows to a transformer, which sends energy through power lines to buildings.

What kind of energy transformation occurs in a generator?

A Mechanical to electrical

B Mechanical to chemical

C Electrical to chemical

D Chemical to electrical

⚜ TEKS 6.11B Understand that gravity is the force that governs the motion of our solar system.

Gravity is a force of attraction between any two objects with mass. The sun and the planets and their moons each exert a gravitational force upon one another. Of all the bodies in the solar system, the sun has the greatest mass, and so it has the greatest gravitational force. Gravitational force decreases with increasing distance between two objects.

Newton's first law of motion states that an object in motion will stay in motion, moving at the same speed in the same direction, unless an unbalanced force acts upon it. Earth, for example, actually travels in a straight line, but the sun's gravitational force pulls it toward the sun. Earth's motion and the sun's gravity keep Earth in orbital motion.

⚜ TEKS Review Question

A company launches a communications satellite around Earth. Which statement about the satellite is true?

F The moon's gravitational force will pull the satellite toward itself.

G Earth's gravitational force will pull the satellite into orbital motion.

H The satellite will continue to move at the same speed in the same direction.

J The sun's gravitational force will eventually draw the satellite out of Earth's orbit.

Grade 6 and 7 Supporting TEKS Review *continued*

🔰 **TEKS 6.12D** Identify the basic characteristics of organisms, including prokaryotic or eukaryotic, unicellular or multicellular, autotrophic or heterotrophic, and mode of reproduction, that further classify them in the currently recognized Kingdoms.

Bacteria belong to the domain Bacteria. Archaea belong to the domain Archaea. Both groups are unicellular prokaryotes, meaning they are made of a single cell with no nucleus. Organisms in the domain Eukarya are placed into one of four kingdoms: protists, fungi, plants, or animals. Protists and fungi may be unicellular or multicellular. Eukaryotes have true membrane-bound nuclei, which hold each cell's DNA, or genetic material.

Bacteria and archaea reproduce asexually, creating offspring identical to the parent. Sexual reproduction occurs in many eukaryotes, resulting in genetic variation.

Methods of obtaining food also vary across kingdoms. Autotrophs, such as plants, are producers, or self-feeding organisms. They use energy sources such as light and inorganic chemicals to make their own food. Heterotrophs, or consumers, feed on producers and other heterotrophs.

🔰 **TEKS Review Question**

The genetic information of a unicellular organism is found inside a membrane-bound nucleus. Which group of organisms does the organism belong to?

A Bacteria

B Protists

C Autotrophs

D Plants

🔰 **TEKS 7.5C** Diagram the flow of energy through living systems, including food chains, food webs, and energy pyramids.

Food chains exist in every ecosystem. These chains often form complex food webs, or interconnected chains. Producers, such as plants, are the foundation of each chain. When consumers eat producers, the chemical energy stored in producers' cells flows to consumers. There are multiple levels of consumers, so energy continues to flow through each level. However, the flow is inefficient. As much as 95% of the chemical energy available at one level never reaches the next highest level. The result is an energy pyramid with a broad base and increasingly less energy available at higher levels.

🔰 **TEKS Review Question**

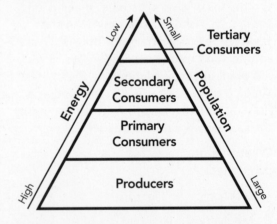

Why does the population at each higher level of the energy pyramid decrease?

F Most food chains lack consumers.

G There is less energy available to organisms at higher levels.

H Producers cannot produce enough food for consumers.

J Human activity affects more populations at higher levels.

TEKS 7.6A Identify that organic compounds contain carbon and other elements such as hydrogen, oxygen, phosphorus, nitrogen, or sulfur.

The majority of chemical compounds are organic compounds. Carbon atoms provide the structure for these compounds. The abundance of organic compounds in the natural world is related to carbon's ability to form stable bonds with thousands of other carbon atoms in a single molecule. In addition to carbon, organic compounds contain hydrogen. They can also contain oxygen, sulfur, nitrogen, and phosphorus.

Living things depend on organic compounds. The fats, proteins, and carbohydrates found in food are organic compounds. So are hormones, vitamins, the hemoglobin in blood, and chlorophyll in plant cells. Until the 1800s, scientists obtained organic chemicals from plants, animals, and fossil fuels. Today, scientists are able to make organic chemicals without depending on living sources.

TEKS Review Question

Which chemical compound in the table is an organic compound?

Chemical Name	Chemical Formula
Sulfur dioxide	SO_2
Methane	CH_4
Ammonia	NH_3
Phosphoric acid	H_3PO_4

A SO_2

B CH_4

C NH_3

D H_3PO_4

TEKS 7.6B Distinguish between physical and chemical changes in matter in the digestive system.

The purpose of digestion is to change large food molecules into molecules small enough for a body's cells to absorb. This process begins in the mouth. As a person chews, teeth cause a physical change as they grind and tear food into smaller pieces. An enzyme in saliva begins the first in a series of chemical changes, as it breaks apart starches into simpler molecules. When a person swallows, muscular contractions in the esophagus push balls of chewed, moist food into the stomach. The stomach releases more enzymes.

After churning food into a semiliquid state, the stomach squeezes food into the small intestine. This is where absorption occurs. Enzymes from the pancreas and bile from the gall bladder enter the small intestine to assist in splitting apart large food molecules into smaller molecules that the body can absorb. The liver filters blood leaving the small intestine. Waste from the small intestine goes to the large intestine to be removed from the body.

TEKS Review Question

In which organs of the digestive system do both physical and chemical changes occur?

F Mouth and stomach

G Liver and gall bladder

H Pancreas and small intestine

J Stomach and pancreas

Grade 6 and 7 Supporting TEKS Review *continued*

TEKS 7.7A Contrast situations where work is done with different amounts of force to situations where no work is done such as moving a box with a ramp and without a ramp, or standing still.

To achieve work, a force moves an object over a distance in the same direction in which the force was exerted. Unless the object moves in the direction of the force, no work is done. Holding a ball, for example, is not work, because the object does not move. Kicking the ball is work, however, because a kick is a force that moves the ball forward.

Lifting a box is work. An upward force displaces the box in an upward direction. The direction of the force and the direction of the displacement are the same. Carrying the box forward is not work, however. That is because the force on the box is upward, but the direction of movement is forward.

TEKS Review Question

In which situation is work done?

A A waiter who is standing up while holding a tray of food above his head

B A parent who is pushing a child forward in a swing

C A mail carrier who is walking forward while carrying a box

D A soccer player whose foot is resting atop a soccer ball

TEKS 7.8C Model the effects of human activity on groundwater and surface water in a watershed.

The effects of human activity on the quality of ground and surface water are broad in both area and time. Effects can be local and swift, or they may cover large areas of land and take years to occur.

Human activities that affect water quality include agriculture, industry, and the growth of cities. On farms and ranches, fertilizers, pesticides, and animal wastes seep into water sources through the ground. They also enter runoff, or excess water that flows into surface water. Industries release chemical waste and heated water into surface water. In cities, people throw garbage into surface water, and underground tanks and pipes leak sewage. Rainwater washes garden fertilizers, pesticides, and pet waste into the watershed. Landfills leak fluids from buried waste, and these fluids can seep into groundwater.

TEKS Review Question

Some gardeners use compost to keep soils rich in nutrients. Compost is organic material created by combining grass clippings, food wastes, and animal manure. It results in a dark black or brown material rich in nutrients. What effect could compost have on water quality?

F It could reduce the need for fertilizers and pesticides that enter groundwater.

G It could lead to more runoff, causing surface waters to overflow their banks.

H It could encourage too much plant growth, which would reduce water levels.

J It could leak harmful chemicals into groundwater.

🔹 TEKS 7.10B Describe how biodiversity contributes to the sustainability of an ecosystem.

Biodiversity refers to the planet's richness and variety of living organisms. The greater Earth's biodiversity, the greater is its health. Greater biodiversity means that ecosystems are populated by larger numbers of species. These species contribute more genetic variation and also provide broader and more stable food webs. They assist in helping ecosystems maintain biogeochemical cycles, such as the water cycle and nutrient cycles. They also help ecosystems function in times of stress. Greater biodiversity, then, makes ecosystems more sustainable.

🔹 TEKS Review Question

A farmer plants fast-growing Crop A on part of his land. The next year, he covers more of his land with Crop A. The crop grows so well that the farmer decides to plant only Crop A. One summer, some plants begin to die from the attack of a harmful virus. The virus spreads quickly, killing almost the entire crop.

What could the farmer have done to avoid this loss?

A Allowed farm animals to graze among the crop

B Planted a greater variety of crops

C Sprayed his crops with pesticides

D Added fertilizer to the soil

🔹 TEKS 7.10C Observe, record, and describe the role of ecological succession such as in a microhabitat of a garden with weeds.

A community is a group of populations living in an area or habitat. A community can be as large as a national park or as small as a puddle. A number of things can disturb a community. Floods, fires, and storms can remove resources and organisms from a habitat. So can human activities. Disturbances are most obvious when all of the vegetation from a habitat is removed.

If left alone, a series of changes begins to occur after a disturbance. Nearby plant species begin to spread. Their growth changes the habitat, making it suitable for other species. Those species eventually replace the original species. The same is true for animal species. Eventually, a climax community forms. This is the final stage of succession, and it may take hundreds of years to form.

🔹 TEKS Review Question

In one region of disturbed land, ecological succession resulted in a climax community of deciduous trees. Which statement about this example of ecological succession is true?

F The same species populate each stage of succession.

G Animal species are the first to repopulate disturbed land.

H Deciduous trees are the first plants to grow in a disturbed area.

J Early species make the environment more suitable for later species.

Grade 6 and 7 Supporting TEKS Review *continued*

🤠 **TEKS 7.11A** Examine organisms or their structures such as insects or leaves and use dichotomous keys for identification.

The word *dichotomous* comes from a Greek word meaning "to cut in two." A dichotomous key offers two choices. In some keys, the choices are yes or no. In others, they are pairs of statements. Only one choice is possible. Each choice takes an observer to another pair of choices. The choices become more and more specific as the process continues. Finally, the choices lead the observer to the identification of an organism.

🤠 **TEKS Review Question**

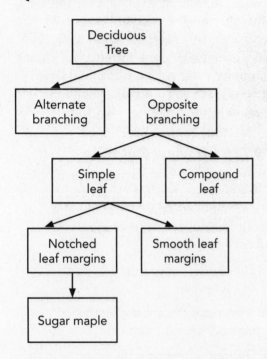

Which statement about this example of a dichotomous key is true?

A It uses yes-or-no questions.

B It uses pairs of characteristics.

C It offers unnecessary information.

D It shows that all deciduous trees are sugar maples.

🤠 **TEKS 7.11C** Identify some changes in genetic traits that have occurred over several generations through natural selection and selective breeding such as the Galápagos Medium Ground Finch (*Geospiza fortis*) or domestic animals.

Some organisms of a species possess traits that are more suited to their environment than others. These organisms reproduce more often. This increases the likelihood that the traits that gave them a reproductive advantage are passed to the next generation. Over several generations, the results of natural selection become observable. For example, several species of finches live on the Galápagos Islands. Variability in physical structure can give some finches advantages in finding food. These finches may reproduce more successfully, passing traits to future generations.

In selective breeding, humans breed organisms that possess desirable traits often leading to new breeds. Such practices may also increase the frequency of disease, as selective breeding can reduce the variability within a population, increasing the frequency of recessive genes linked to disease.

🤠 **TEKS Review Question**

Which of the following describes a situation in which a genetic change has caused a change in a population over several generations?

F Two purple pea plants producing an offspring with white flowers

G Two red horses producing gold-colored offspring three years in a row

H Average beak size in a bird population increasing in response to increased availability of hard seeds

J A four-leafed clover stem appearing occasionally in three-leafed clover plants

🦅 **TEKS 7.12B** Identify the main functions of the systems of the human organism, including the circulatory, respiratory, skeletal, muscular, digestive, excretory, reproductive, integumentary, nervous, and endocrine systems.

In the human body, the heart pumps blood through a circulatory system of vessels. The blood carries gases and nutrients to body cells and carries waste away. The lungs of the respiratory system contain millions of tiny air sacs, where gases move across membranes into and from the blood. The bones of the skeletal system provide support, structure, and protection. The muscular system allows movement. The digestive system, which includes the stomach and intestines, changes food molecules into smaller molecules that can be delivered to body cells. The excretory system, which includes the lungs, kidneys, and bladder, removes waste from the body. The reproductive system makes it possible to produce offspring. The integumentary system, or skin, is the first line of defense against harmful invaders. The nervous system delivers messages to and from the brain. The endocrine system directs growth and maintains the body through the release of chemical messengers called hormones.

🦅 **TEKS Review Question**

Among its many effects on human body systems, cigarette smoking raises blood pressure and tightens blood vessels. It decreases blood flow to fingers and toes and reduces the amount of oxygen blood can carry. Which system is affected directly by these examples?

A Digestive

B Excretory

C Circulatory

D Reproductive

🦅 **TEKS 7.12D** Differentiate between structure and function in plant and animal cell organelles, including cell membrane, cell wall, nucleus, cytoplasm, mitochondrion, chloroplast, and vacuole.

Plant and animal cells are surrounded by cell membranes. Inside, the cells are filled with cytoplasm, a fluid-like substance. Organelles, or "little organs," are suspended in the cytoplasm. The largest organelle in plant and animal cells is usually the nucleus, where most of the cell's genetic information is stored. The organelles also include ribosomes, which build proteins. The endoplasmic reticulum, or ER, is a system of connected tunnels and sacs. Smooth ER builds molecules called lipids and breaks down toxins. Rough ER makes proteins and builds membrane material.

Unlike animal cells, a plant cell has a cell wall. This wall shapes and protects plant cells. Plant cells also have a central vacuole that takes up to 80% of the space in a cell. Vacuoles store materials and contribute to plant growth and protection. Plant cells also have chloroplasts, where light energy from the sun is converted into chemical energy stored in sugar molecules.

🦅 **TEKS Review Question**

A student examines a cell through a microscope. A large organelle takes up most of the space within the cell, and numerous green, oval-shaped structures are visible. What kind of cell is the student examining?

F Plant cell

G Bacterium

H Animal cell

J Prokaryotic cell

Grade 6 and 7 Supporting TEKS Review *continued*

🔖 **TEKS 7.12F** Recognize that according to cell theory all organisms are composed of cells and cells carry on similar functions such as extracting energy from food to sustain life.

Cell theory states that all living things are made of cells. The cell is the basic unit, or building block, of life. Whether they form a single-celled or multicellular organism, all cells share certain characteristics, and they function in similar ways.

Cells divide to form new cells. So, all cells come from pre-existing cells. Each cell passes DNA, which contains hereditary information, to its daughter cells. Cell division also enables organisms to grow and repair themselves.

🔖 **TEKS Review Question**

Which statement forms the foundation of cell theory?

A Cells contain genetic material.

B All living organisms are made of cells.

C The basic chemistry of all cells is the same.

D The cells of unicellular and multicellular organisms share characteristics.

🔖 **TEKS 7.14B** Compare the results of uniform or diverse offspring from sexual reproduction or asexual reproduction.

There is only one parent in asexual reproduction. During asexual reproduction, a cell undergoes mitosis. Daughter cells have the identical genetic information as the parent. Unicellular organisms primarily undergo asexual reproduction, but some multicellular organisms also reproduce asexually. A hydra, for example, reproduces by budding. A bud is a cluster of cells that divide through mitosis.

Sexual reproduction requires two parents. Each parent contributes genetic information to the offspring. This shuffling of genetic information leads to greater variation among offspring. The offspring have unique combinations of their parents' genetic information.

🔖 **TEKS Review Question**

Some Types of Asexual Reproduction	
Budding	Offspring grow out of the parent's body.
Fragmentation	A parent's body breaks into pieces, each of which can produce offspring.
Regeneration	A part of a parent breaks off, grows, and develops into a new individual.
Parthenogenesis	An unfertilized egg develops into an individual.

An organism separates into two pieces. Both pieces produce new individuals. Which method of asexual reproduction occurred?

F Budding

G Fragmentation

H Regeneration

J Parthenogenesis

TEKS 7.14C Recognize that inherited traits of individuals are governed in the genetic material found in the genes within chromosomes in the nucleus.

A gene is an inherited unit of information. Genes are found within strands of DNA contained in chromosomes. Each kind of eukaryote has a unique number of chromosomes. Most cells in humans, for example, contain 23 pairs, or 46 chromosomes. These chromosomes are in a eukaryotic cell's nucleus, or control center.

Humans inherit tens of thousands of genes from their parents. Each gene is like an instruction manual for operating a machine. It directs cells to build certain proteins. These proteins direct cell activity and determine an individual's specific characteristics.

TEKS Review Question

A scientist observes the process of mitosis through a microscope. During metaphase, 27 pairs of chromosomes line up along the center of the cell. What kind of cell is the scientist observing?

Species	Number of Chromosomes
Cat	38
Sheep	54
Horse	64
Dog	78

A Cat

B Sheep

C Horse

D Dog

Test-Taking Strategies
For the Texas End-of-Year Test

Multiple-choice questions make up much of end-of-course assessment tests. So, you need to become an expert at deciphering multiple-choice questions.

We have included a variety of strategies that will help you. You will not need to use all of these strategies for every question.

In a multiple-choice question, several possible answers are given to you, and you need to figure out which one of those answers is best. The first part of the question is called the stem. The stem can be a question or an incomplete statement. Read the stem carefully before you look at the answer choices.

The answer choices are indicated by letters A, B, C, D or F, G, H, J. One answer choice is correct. The other answer choices, called distractors, are incorrect.

STRATEGY Sequencing Events

Some test questions require you to arrange a series of events in order. For example, you might be asked which event comes first or last. Before looking at the answer choices, try to determine the correct sequence in which the events occur.

Sample Question 1

Composite volcanoes form on a continental plate in a sequence of steps. Which of the following is the first step toward forming this type of volcano?

A Subduction occurs.

B Crust above the subducting plate melts and forms magma.

C An oceanic plate collides with a continental plate.

D A deep-ocean trench forms.

C is correct. **A** cannot be correct because subduction can only occur if a trench has formed. You can eliminate **B** because the formation of magma occurs near the end of the process. **D** cannot be correct because two plates must collide before a trench can form.

Sample Question 2

What is the correct sequence of events that changes particles of liquid into gas during evaporation?

F Temperature increases, particles move faster, particles break free from defined volume

G Temperature increases, particles break free from defined volume, particles move faster

H Particles break free from defined volume, particles move faster, temperature increases

J Particles move faster, particles break free from defined volume, temperature increases

The correct answer is **F**. Choices **H** and **J** can be eliminated because evaporation starts with a temperature increase. **G** is also incorrect because in order to break free from the liquid, the particles must increase their speed.

STRATEGY Reading All the Answer Choices

When you answer a multiple-choice question, always read *every* answer choice before selecting an answer. One choice may be more complete than another choice, which may be only partially correct. Also, *all of the above* may be a possible answer. If you stop reading as soon as you find an answer that seems correct, you won't notice that *all of the above* is an option.

Sample Question 1

The troposphere is the layer of the atmosphere

A in which Earth's weather occurs.

B that is closest to Earth's surface.

C that contains most of the mass of the atmosphere.

D all of the above

If you know that Earth's weather occurs in the troposphere, you might be tempted to stop reading and select choice **A.** However choices **B** and **C** are also true. Therefore, the most complete answer is **D,** all of the above.

Sample Question 2

On the periodic table, chlorine (Cl) can be found

F in Group 17.

G with the halogens.

H both F and G

J none of the above

Choice **H** is correct. You may have chosen **F** or **G** if you did not read all the answer choices correctly. Also, be careful not to assume that choices like **J,** none of the above, are always the correct answer.

Test-Taking Strategies
For the Texas End-of-Year Test *continued*

STRATEGY Using Formulas

Some test questions require you to use a formula to answer a question. For example, in Sample Question 1 below, you should recall that speed can be found using the following formula:

$$\text{Speed} = \frac{\text{distance}}{\text{time}}$$

To solve for a quantity in a formula, substitute known values, including units, for the variables. Be sure to include units in your final answer.

Sample Question 1

An island on the Pacific plate moves a distance of 550 cm in 50 years. What is the plate's rate of speed?

A 44 cm per year

B 110 cm per year

C 2,750 cm per year

D 11 cm per year

The answer is **D**.

$$\frac{550 \text{ cm}}{50 \text{ years}} = 11 \text{ cm per year}$$

Plug each known value into the formula and complete the math. Use the units to figure out which value goes where. For example, centimeters are distance units and years are time units.

Sample Question 2

Density can be found by dividing an object's mass by its volume $\left(D = \frac{m}{v}\right)$. What is the density of a sample of tin with a mass of 36.5 g and a volume of 5.0 cm³?

F 1.4 g/cm³

G 7.3 g/cm³

H 31.5 g/cm³

J 182.5 cm³/g

G is the correct answer.

$$\frac{36.5 \text{ g}}{5.0 \text{ cm}^3} = \frac{7.3 \text{ g}}{\text{cm}^3}$$

Be careful of incorrect answer choices like **J**. The units for this choice are incorrect when the density formula has been used correctly to solve the problem.

STRATEGY Interpreting Graphs

A bar graph is used to compare quantities of different things. Each bar represents a quantity or amount of something. When answering a question with a bar graph, keep the following tips in mind. Read the title of the graph. The title helps you identify what information is shown on the graph. Then carefully examine the labels on the axes to determine what variables are measured.

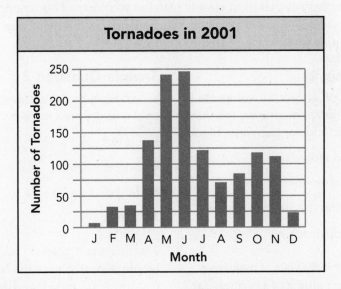

Tornadoes in 2001

Sample Question 1

Use the graph to determine how many tornadoes occurred in January.

A 30

B 25

C 5

D 15

First find the J for January on the *x*-axis. Then check the height of the bar and determine on the *y*-axis how many tornadoes occurred. The correct answer is choice **C**.

Sample Question 2

Which month had fewer than 100 tornadoes?

F April

G June

H September

J November

The correct answer is **H**. To find the answer using the graph, find 100 on the *y*-axis. Then find which months' bars are below that line. Of the answer choices, only September's bar is below the 100 line of the *y*-axis.

Test-Taking Strategies

For the Texas End-of-Year Test *continued*

STRATEGY Anticipating the Answer

You may be able to figure out the answer to a question before looking at the answer choices. After thinking of your own answer, compare it with the choices provided. Select the answer that most closely matches your own. This strategy can be especially useful for questions that test vocabulary. Try to answer the questions below before looking at the answer choices.

Sample Question 1

Which two pieces of laboratory equipment would be most useful for measuring the mass and volume of a rectangular aluminum block?

A Metric ruler and stopwatch

B Balance and metric ruler

C Thermometer and graduated cylinder

D Balance and stopwatch

The correct answer is **B.** Mass is measured with a balance. The volume of a rectangular solid is found by multiplying length × width × height, which are measured with a metric ruler. Choices **A** and **D** each contain only one of the necessary pieces of equipment. A stopwatch measures time. In Choice **C,** the graduated cylinder measures volume, but a thermometer measures temperature, not mass.

Sample Question 2

Which term best describes an extremely cold and dry area covered in permafrost?

F Desert

G Boreal forest

H Taiga

J Tundra

J is the correct answer choice. The tundra biome is located near the North Pole. Choices **F, G,** and **H** are also terrestrial biomes, but they are not characterized by extreme cold, low precipitation, and the presence of permafrost. If you anticipated tundra as the answer before reading the choices, then you can be fairly confident that you were correct.

STRATEGY Paying Attention to the Details

Sometimes two or more answers to a question are almost identical. If you do not read the answers carefully, you may select an incorrect answer by mistake. In the questions below, all the answer choices are similar. Read the questions and the answer choices carefully before choosing the correct answer.

Sample Question 1

The name for the compound with the formula $CaCl_2$ is

A calcium(II) chloride.

B calcium chlorine.

C calcium dichloride.

D calcium chloride.

The correct answer is **D.** Choices **A, B,** and **C** include the correct elements in the correct order—metal before nonmetal. However, only **D** uses the correct rules for naming $CaCl_2$.

Sample Question 2

Which method of heat transfer moves thermal energy from a hot frying pan into food when cooking?

F Conduction

G Subduction

H Convection

J Induction

F is correct. You can eliminate **G** and **J** because they are not forms of heat transfer, even though the words sound similar to heat transfer vocabulary. Choice **H** is also incorrect because convection is heat transfer through air or water, but food is cooked in a frying pan through direct contact.

Test-Taking Strategies

For the Texas End-of-Year Test *continued*

STRATEGY Narrowing the Choices

If after reading all the answer choices you are not sure which one is correct, eliminate those answers that you know are wrong. For example, in Sample Question 1 below, first eliminate the answers that require a whole number. Then focus on the remaining choices.

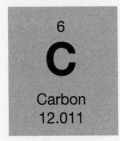

6

C

Carbon
12.011

Sample Question 1

The number 12.011 is the

A atomic number for carbon.

B percentage of carbon-12 in nature.

C atomic mass of carbon-12.

D average atomic mass of carbon.

D is the correct answer. Choice **A** can be eliminated first because it is a whole number. **B** can also be eliminated because 12.011 is not a percentage. Then, you only have to choose between **C** and **D** for the correct answer.

Sample Question 2

Ganymede is the largest moon of

F Mercury.

G Venus.

H Jupiter.

J Neptune.

The correct answer is **H.** You can eliminate **F** and **G** because those planets do not have moons at all. Once the choices are narrowed down to two, **J** can be eliminated because Ganymede does not revolve around Neptune.

STRATEGY Interpreting Diagrams

On some tests, you may be asked questions about a diagram. Understanding the information in the diagram is the key to answering the question correctly. When you are shown a diagram, examine it carefully. Look at the objects and symbols in the diagram and read the labels. Use the diagram below to answer the sample questions.

Sample Question 1

What conclusion can you draw by looking at the diagram?

A Air resistance in front of the balloon pushes it backwards.

B Gravity forces air out of the balloon's open end.

C The force of the air leaving the balloon propels it forward.

D Friction causes the balloon's acceleration to decrease.

The diagram shows a pair of action-reaction forces. The action force is caused by the balloon pushing out air. According to Newton's third law of motion, the reaction force of the air pushes on the balloon, propelling it forward. The correct answer is choice **C.**

Sample Question 2

Which direction is the reaction force in?

F upward

G to the left

H in the direction of gravity

J in the same direction as motion

The correct answer is **J.** The reaction force results in the balloon's motion, so it is in the same direction as movement. On the diagram, it is represented by the force arrow pointing to the right.

take note

this space is yours—great for drawing diagrams and making notes